Fixed and Flat

PHIL PANTANA

FIXED

AND

FLAT

Scriptural Support & Scientific Evidence

publishers
SOLUTION
The Key to Publishing and Printing Possibilities

Fixed and Flat
Scriptural Support & Scientific Evidence

ISBN 978-1-937925-37-6 paperback

Cover Design by:
Megan Dillon
megan@creativeninjadesigns.com

Interior Design by:
Christopher Kirk
www.GFSstudio.com

publishers
SOLUTION
The Key to Publishing and Printing Possibilities

"When the Christian layman in Geology or Astronomy finds a discrepancy between the Scriptures and what confronts him as a result of scientific work, the proper thing for him to do is to abide by the Scripture and lay that thing of science aside as erroneous."

Dr. A. L. Graebner, Quarterly VI, 42.

"Unproven assumptions that are required to explain phenomena that are readily explained without the assumptions constitute false science."

Marshall Hall

"The Bible was not written to teach men science, but the Bible is scientifically accurate."

Dr. Bob Jones, Sr.

"Sometimes people don't want to hear the truth because they don't want their illusions destroyed."

Friedrich Nietzsche

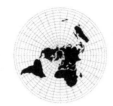

TABLE OF CONTENTS

Science is Knowledge

The Scientific Method

B.I.B.L.E.—Basic Instructions Before Leaving Earth

Only Two Worldviews

Psalm 19

Complete Education

The Principal Discovery

Some Preliminaries

Foundational Knowledge

The Importance of Genesis

History Is His Story

Genesis Foundation

Origins by Design

Five Ultimate Scientific Ideas

The Modes of God's Self-Revelation

Three Reasons Why God Created

What Faulkner Believes
God's Word, the Authority!
Be Careful What You Believe

PREFACE

Somebody Bigger Than You and I
Johnny Lange, Hy Heath, and Sonny Burke

Who made the mountains? Who made the trees?
Who made the rivers flow to the sea?
And who sends the rain when the earth is dry?
Somebody bigger than you and I

Who made the flowers to bloom in the Spring?
Who made the song for the robins to sing?
And who hung the moon and the stars in the sky?
Somebody bigger than you and I

He lights the way when the road is long
He keeps you company
And with His love to guide you
He walks beside you
Just like He walks with me

When I am weary, filled with despair

Who gives me courage to go on from there?
And who gives me faith that will never die
Somebody bigger than you and I

I Sing the Mighty Power
Isaac Watts

I sing the mighty power of God
That makes the mountains rise
That spread the flowing seas abroad
And built the lofty skies
I sing the wisdom that ordained
The sun to rule the day
The moon shines full at His command
And all the stars obey

I sing the goodness of the Lord
That filled the earth with food
He formed the creatures with His Word
And then pronounced them good
Lord, how thy wonders are displayed
Where'er I turn my eye
If I survey the ground I tread
Or gaze upon the sky

There's not a plant or flower below
But makes thy glories known
And clouds arise and tempests blow
By order from Thy throne
While all that borrows life from thee
Is ever in Thy care
And everywhere that man can be
Thou God art present there!

Amen, amen!

For the Beauty of the Earth
Folliott S. Pierpoint

For the beauty of the earth,
for the glory of the skies,
for the love which from our birth
over and around us lies.

Refrain:
Christ, our Lord, to you we raise
this, our hymn of grateful praise.

For the wonder of each hour
of the day and of the night,
hill and vale and tree and flower,
sun and moon and stars of light, [Refrain]

For the joy of human love,
brother, sister, parent, child,
friends on earth, and friends above,
for all gentle thoughts and mild, [Refrain]

For yourself, best gift divine,
to the world so freely given,
agent of God's grand design:
peace on earth and joy in heaven. [Refrain]

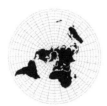

INTRODUCTION

One believes things because one has been conditioned to believe them.
~Aldous Huxley

What have you been conditioned to believe about the Earth, the Sun, the Moon, the Stars, and the Heavens? Have you been brainwashed to NOT investigate? Have you been indoctrinated or educated? Do you have a biblical Christian worldview? Do you believe Genesis 1:1?

Do you believe Science or Scripture? Do know the facts or do you believe in an unprovable theory? Have you been bamboozled? Have you been conditioned to believe the Earth is spinning? Or, do you believe the Sun moves and is orbiting the non-moving Earth? Have you been conditioned to believe in a round ball earth? A spherical globe?

Do you know that there is Scriptural support and scientific evidence to prove that we live on a nonmoving earth? Do you know that the earth is a flat plane and round like a coin? Do you know the North Pole is the center of the Earth? Do you know our Earth is a huge pond within the Antarctic rim and covered by a transparent glass dome? Do you have an open mind and a receptive heart to believe the truth? Stop! Take the time to think things through. The truth will set you free.

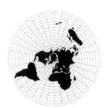

THE PURPOSE

The purpose of this book is twofold:

1. to argue for the Geocentric model of the Earth and show with biblical support and empirical scientific evidence that Geocentrism is both a biblical and scientific explanation. Arguing for geocentrism is not to reject science for Scripture.
2. to argue that the Earth is a flat plane and not a globe or round ball.

Avoiding Truth

"There is a principle which is a bar against all information, which is proof against all argument, and which cannot fail to keep man in everlasting ignorance. That principle is condemnation before investigation."
Edmund Spencer

The Path to Folly

"He who answers a matter before he hears it. It is folly and shame to him."
Proverbs 18:13 NKJV

Hear the Matter Out

> "Shouting off before listening to the facts
> is both shameful and foolish."
> *Proverb 18:13 NLT*

Epistemology

The term "epistemology" comes from two Greek words: "episteme" and "logos." "Episteme" is translated as "knowledge." Greek: ginosko "to know" (1097). "Logos" is translated as "argument" or "reason."

Epistemology is the theory of knowledge. Epistemology is the investigation of what distinguishes justified belief from opinion. Epistemology is how we know what we know.

Occam's Razor

The simplest explanation tends to be the truth.

Sherlock Holmes

> *"When the impossible has been eliminated, whatever is left,
> however improbable must be the truth."*

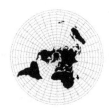

BIBLICAL CHRISTIAN WORLDVIEW

A biblical Christian worldview, in order to be considered truly biblical, must believe and defend the Doctrine of Creation (Genesis record), the geocentric model (earth is non-moving), and the flat earth model (earth is a plane with a dome).

Enemies within the church are now corrupting and destroying churches, Bible Colleges, Christian Universities, and Seminaries all around the world by teaching Darwinian evolution, the heliocentric model, and the global spherical model.

Science Is Knowledge

"The fear of the LORD is the beginning of knowledge."
Proverbs 1:7 ESV

Science means knowledge. The fear of Yahweh (LORD: Hebrew Yahweh) is the only basis of true knowledge. The "fear" is reverential awe and worshipful response of faith to our living Creator. The "fear of the LORD" means living in covenant relationship with the God of grace and glory. The beginning of knowledge means its basic, ruling principle. The instruction form of wisdom begins with a call to attentiveness or meticulous research.

The Scientific Method

The scientific method is an empirical method of acquiring knowledge. A theory or opinion is put forward that matches what we observe. The scientific method first involves careful observation, then rigorous skepticism is applied about what is observed. The experiment is repeated and the results are compared. To form a correct conclusion, the data must support the hypothesis. Then the hypothesis can be explained for the phenomena.

B.I.B.L.E.—BASIC INSTRUCTIONS BEFORE LEAVING EARTH

We must traffic in TRUTH. When it comes to truth, tolerance is a mockery of truth. Secular humanists deny truth exists. Sir Charles Lyell (1797-1875) was the foremost British geologist of his day. His aim was to free science of Moses. If you won't believe Moses you won't believe Jesus.

The Bible is God's user guide to the world. Finding True North without the compass of the Bible is impossible.

Only Two World Views

Everything is a result of a cosmic accident (time and chance).
We are the result of a deliberate design by an Intelligent Designer.
Four Basic Questions

- Who am I ?
- Where did I come from?
- Why am I here?
- Where am I going when I die?

Science vs. Scripture

- Where do you gain your knowledge?
- Do you rely on "Science says" or "Scripture says?"

Psalm 19

Psalm 19 illustrates the two general categories of revelation:

1. Natural Revelation: God's revealing of Himself through the created order (vv. 1-6)
2. Special Revelation: God's revealing of Himself through the Scriptures (vv. 7-11)

Psalm 19 is divided into two parts. In Part One the message of the stars is given. In Part Two the message of Yahweh's Word is given. Part One is set against Part Two in such a way that David is saying that the message in the stars and the message in the Scriptures are one and the same. The internal structure joins both halves together in one complete Psalm. The shepherd had studied both the heavens and the Law and found in them the same Truth. Amen!

THE BIBLE IS, FROM GENESIS TO REVELATION, A GEOCENTRIC BOOK !!!
THE BIBLE IS, FROM GENESIS TO REVELATION, A FLAT-EARTH BOOK !!!
THE EARTH IS FIXED. IT IS NON-MOVING!
THE EARTH IS NOT SPINNING AT 1,038 mph.
THE EARTH IS NOT ROTATING AROUND THE SUN AT 67,000 mph.

Complete Education

No person's education is complete if they do not know and understand their Bible. The essential completeness has been outlawed in our government schools. Many school children are in enforced paganism. We all need to repair our own illiteracy about the Bible and help others to know and understand the biblical accounts about creation, about redemption (to be bought back), and the fulfillment of God's divine promises.

"It is impossible to rightly govern the world without God and the Bible."
George Washington

"I believe the Bible is the best gift God has ever given to man. All the good from the Savior of the world is communicated to us through this book."
Abe Lincoln

"The Bible is worth all the other books which have ever been printed."
Patrick Henry

"The Bible is no mere book, but it is a Living Creature, with a power that conquers all that oppose it."
Napoleon

"For the Word of God is living and active, sharper than any two-edged sword, piercing to the division of soul and spirit, of joints and of marrow, and discerning the thoughts and intentions of the heart."
Hebrews 4:12 ESV

"If we abide by the principles taught in the Bible, our country will go on prospering and to prosper. But if we and our posterity neglect its instructions and authority, no man can tell how sudden a catastrophe may overwhelm us and bury all our glory in profound obscurity."
Daniel Webster

"Jack of all trades, master of One."
"A cultured person is one who knows something about everything and everything about something."
Ben Franklin

*"I have sworn upon the altar of God eternal hostility against
every form of tyranny over the mind of man."*
Thomas Jefferson

Can educators and churches pledge anything less?
A Christian's specialization must be the Bible. You're reading this book is a key step in correcting biblical illiteracy.

What's Ahead:
The ultimate biblical and scientific adventure

- The Miracle of our Origin
- The Mystery of our Destiny

Creation (Genesis account), Astronomy (geocentric model) , and Cosmology (flat-earth model)
We are engaged in a cosmic war - Ephesians 6:12-13

The Principal Discovery

The 66 books in the Bible were penned by 40 different authors written in three different languages in 13 different countries and in three different continents over a period of 1,600 years. We have in our possession an Integrated Message System. Every detail is there by design. There is an integrity of the whole. It demonstrably has its origin from outside our dimension of time. It writes history in advance. The text anticipates accurate information that emerges thousands of years later.

Two Critical Discoveries

1. The Bible's design is composed of an intricate, skillfully designed Integrated Message System. Every detail is there by deliberate design.
2. The Bible's design demonstrably has its origin from outside our time domain.

Some Preliminaries

Shed the baggage of our misconceptions about the geocentric model and the flat-earth model

We live in a Finite Universe. The universe had a beginning around 6,000 years ago. The word "universe" comes from two words:

- uni = single
- verse = spoken sentence

We live in a single spoken sentence. God said, "Let there be" and there was. The Hebrew calendar started at the time of creation, placed at 3761 BC. The Year of Man in the Hebrew year, anno mundi or AM, is 5781 BC. Anno Mundi began at sunset on 18 September 4004 BC on the Gregorian calendar.

Foundational Knowledge

> If the foundations are destroyed, what can the righteous do?
> *Psalm 11:3*

Society depends on moral foundations.

Psalm 11:3 sets forth the foundational knowledge upon which our moral framework is built.

If the foundations of a society are undermined, then what can good and righteous men do to prevent its collapse?

The Importance of Genesis

The Bible is the key to our understanding the universe and its form and the mannishness of man. Without this key our observations are out of perspective; we do not know what we are looking at. All the information given in the Bible flows out of the information given in the first eleven chapters of Genesis.

Unless we are told about the beginning, we cannot make sense of the present. This is where Genesis Chapters 1 to 11 are so important. These chapters give the history that comes before anything that secular historians have been able to ascertain. Biblical history is pre-secular history, which gives meaning to mankind's present history.

The first eleven chapters of Genesis are the very foundation on which all knowledge rests. Before the creation of the universe, the infinite-personal God existed and He spoke the universe (the space-time continuum) into existence by choice, ex Logos. The Creation was not without a cause.

The infinite-personal God was its cause. He chose to create. He willed to create, and "it was" (Revelation 4:11).

History Is His Story

Christianity involves history. The Judeo-Christian world view is rooted in history. The Bible is accepted as a literal, true record of history. The Bible tells us how God communicated with man in history from BC to AD. God has intervened in earth history on many occasions, including miracles and supernatural weather modification: the Flood of Noah, ten plagues of Egypt, fire from heaven upon Sodom and Gomorrah, and calming the sea.

Yahweh Elohim is revealed to us in the Scriptures. He claims not only to be the Truth but to be able to reveal truth to those who seek Him. The most profound question a person could ask is: "What is Truth?" The problem is: Will you recognize truth if and when you see it? The historicity of persons and events connected with the great Flood described in the early chapters of Genesis is confirmed in six passages in the NT. This is history. The battle between the humanist world view and the biblical Christian world view is the battle between man determining truth for himself and God's Word being the ultimate truth. From God's Word we learn: the meaning of life, standards for life, marriage for life, laws for life, and the creation of life.

Genesis Foundation

The Book of Genesis is foundational to a right understanding of the rest of the Bible, all Christian doctrine, and the development of a proper worldview. The order of creation is found in the first two chapters of Genesis. Here is the root of all truth and reality in time and space. Creation is a cardinal doctrine of the Christian faith. The Bible begins with the most essential element in the order of creation - God. According to John Calvin, creation is the "whole workmanship of the universe." Creation reveals the intelligent design and glory of God displayed in living color day after day.

To attack the foundational book of origins is an attempt to destroy the very foundation upon which we build the very structures of our life. If we allow Genesis 1-11 to be turned into some mythology or metaphor, or if we allow the order of creation to be used in reverse order, then we have no solid foundation upon which the ethical pillars of our worldview structure can stand in the midst of political, pagan, and demonic domains.

Origins by Design

If there is incredible design, then there must be an Intelligent Designer.

"In the beginning the Intelligent Designer created the heavens and the earth."
Pantana Translation
Genesis - The Beginning

"In the beginning God created the heavens and the earth."
Genesis 1:1 ESV

Five Ultimate Scientific Ideas

Evolutionary philosopher Herbert Spencer outlined five "ultimate scientific ideas" which comprise everything that is susceptible to scientific examination.

Five categories:

- time
- force
- action
- space
- and matter.

Genesis 1:1 accounts for all five categories:

- In the beginning = time
- God = force/power

- created = action
- the heavens = space
- the earth = matter

The Modes of God's Self-Revelation
- General/Natural Revelation
- Incarnation/In Son Revelation
- Scripture/Special Verbal Revelation

Three Reasons Why God Created
1. For His Own Glory
2. For His Own Pleasure
3. For His Fellowship With Man

Biblical Metaphysical Dualism

Uncreated Reality	Created Reality
The Triune God	Time Space Matter

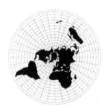

FOUR BASIC QUALITIES IN CREATION

1. Matter   3. Information
2. Energy   4. Will (Volition)

Evidence of God's Existence From Design

Divine Watchmaker
William Paley

If there is a watch, there must be a watchmaker.
If there is a world, there must be a world maker.

The existence of God as creator is evident in His creation (Romans 1:18-22). In Acts 17:18-34, Paul presents God as Creator, Giver of all, and ruler of nations and history, and as One who seeks man's love, which consists not in idol worship but in turning from sin.

There is coming a day when everyone will be judged by God through the resurrected Yeshua. His resurrection gives public proof that the Gospel is true and therefore objectively demands belief.

There Are Only Two Choices

1. 1. Somebody (Creator) made the world.
2. 2. The world made itself.

> *"Humanists regard the Universe as self existing and not created."*
> Humanist Manifesto 1 (1933) Tenant #1
> [Notice the capital "U" to deify universe]

God is Timeless

God is outside of our of time domain. There are no clocks or calendars in heaven. 2 Peter 3:8 states: "With the Lord a day is like a thousand years, and a thousand years are like a day." Peter quoted from Psalm 90:4. 'Like' or 'as' are figures of speech, called a simile. This teaches that God is outside of our time domain. The day is literal and is contrasted with 1,000 years. A short period of time and a longer period of time are the same to an eternal God. The context has nothing to do with the days of creation. Compromising half-time Creationists teach that the days in Genesis are 1,000 years long based on this simile. What is this verse saying? God is not bound by time as we are. God is outside of our time domain. He is the Creator of time itself. In the beginning = time.

Uncreated Reality

God is uncreated reality. God is the first cause. God is the uncaused cause.

Created Reality

In the beginning God created...
Heavens and Earth
Angels, Plants, Stars
Man
Animal Kingdom
Plant Kingdom
Inanimate Objects

Earth Was Designed
> For Life
> To Be Inhabited
> As A Home For Man

Two Triads of Days

Creation was broken into two triads of days. During the first three days of creation God's work was focused on earth. From the beginning God made earth for man to inhabit - a home.

The fundamental structures of creation:

1. Earth
2. Sun
3. Moon
4. Stars
5. Firmament (Sky)
6. Land
7. Man

Three Heavens

In beginning, Elohim created three heavens. Heavens (shamayim, the Hebrew word for heavens; -im ending is plural); a three-part biblical cosmology.

First heaven is where birds and bees and airplanes fly and clouds roll.
Second heaven is where the Sun, the Moon, and the Stars circle the Earth.
Sun - circles Earth every 24hrs...
Moon - circles Earth every 24hrs 50min 28sec...
Stars - circle Earth every 23hrs 56min 4sec...
all orbit east-to-west.

Third Heaven

The realm of God, above the glass ceiling - the sky. The sky is thick hard transparent glass to hold the water above the expanse. The expanse is firm or hardened glass. We get the word firmament from this. Water is above the sky. That's why it's blue. The expanse is not the atmosphere.

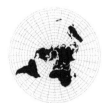

THE WORLD'S GREATEST LIBRARY

66 books in the Bible (Route 66)
39 books in the OT or Old Covenant
27 books in the NT or New Covenant
1,189 chapters in the Bible
31,173 verses in the Bible

The Most Important Verse in the Bible

"In the beginning God created the heavens and the earth."
Genesis 1:1

Hebrew Text Transliterated (Genesis 1:1) Bereshit bara Elohim et hasha-mayim ve'et ha'aretz.

The first verse of Genesis has seven Hebrew words and 28 letters. The Hebrew language is written from right to left. All languages flow toward Jerusalem. The Torah always points to YHWH. If you believe this verse is true, then you will have no problem believing that the rest of the Bible is true.

The Most Important Chapters in the Bible

Genesis 1 - 11

All the major doctrines are found in the first 11 chapters of Genesis.

Who Wrote the Torah?

Moses. Jesus said so.

In Luke 24:13-16, on Resurrection Sunday, Jesus appeared as a stranger to Cleopas and his wife Mary on the Emmaus Road. That afternoon they walked together for 7-1/2 miles to their home. In verse 27, Jesus began with Moses and all the Prophets. He interpreted to them in all the Scriptures the things concerning Himself.

Believe Moses

> "Yes it isn't I who will accuse you before the Father,
> Moses will accused you! Yes, Moses, in whom you put your
> hopes. If you really believed Moses, you would believe me,
> because he wrote about me. But since you don't believe
> what he wrote, how will you believe what I say?"
> *John 5:45-47 NLT*

Hidden Codes in the Bible

> "It is God's privilege to conceal things
> and the king's privilege to discover them."
> *Proverbs 25:2 NLT*

Creation Week

Sunday - Day One	"Let light be"
Monday - Day Two	Stretching of Space
Tuesday - Day Three	Land and Vegetation
Wednesday - Day Four	Sun, Moon, Stars
Thursday - Day Five	Sea animals and Birds
Friday - Day Six	Land animals and Man

I AM Witness

Does observational science confirm that the world was created by God? YES. Are there trustworthy documents and eyewitness accounts that confirm it? YES.

Was anybody there to observe the creation of the world? YES. The Triune God was and He told us how He created it. God inspired 40 authors to write down His very words that became individual books that were compiled into a complete book called the Bible, which has been verified over and over again and has demonstrated itself totally trustworthy in all it claims and teachings. The Bible accurately records historical events. The Bible is a supernatural book. It is extra-terrestrial in origin. It came to us outside of our time domain. We have the most trustworthy revelation from the most trustworthy eyewitness - the great I AM.

Does observational science confirm the Bible? YES. The observable fact is that the universe is both logical and orderly. That makes sense only if its creator is logical and has imposed order on His creation. The earth is not an accident of a huge explosion. Our minds are capable of comprehending many things about the universe. That's only possible if the creator of the mind gave us the ability and desire to explore the universe. Our brains are not by-products of chance, otherwise we couldn't trust the conclusions to ever be accurate.

We can only observe and repeat an experiment if the universe consistently obeys the same laws day after day. This only makes sense if the Lawgiver created it that way and upholds it.

Birthplace of Life

Clay is the infertile blend of minerals. The clay is a blend of complex bio-chemicals that make life possible. Clay is the birthplace of life on Earth. God formed the man out of soft pliable reddish clay along the riverbank outside of the Garden of Eden. Adam was the first man on earth and the first man of color. His skin tone was reddish-brown, like that of the American Indians. Oklahoma is a Choctaw Indian word that means "red people." It comes from two words: people (okla) and red (humma).

Adam literally means "red" or "son of the red Earth." The Hebrew word is "adamah" meaning "earth," from which Adam was formed. The word *Adamah* translates "red clay" or "red ground" which reinforces the teleological (purpose) link between all humankind and the ground. Man is both made from the *adamah* and inhabits it. That's why grounding works. Mud baths are considered therapeutic for the skin, muscles, joints and mind. Tell your kids to go play in the mud. There is a connection.

The Bible informs us that the LORD God (Elohim) formed the man from the dust of the ground and breathed into his nostrils the breath of life, and the man became a living being (Genesis 2:7). Elohim did two things in creating man. First, He formed man from the very dust of the ground—the infertile blend of minerals. Second, He breathed His own breath into the two nostrils of Adam. A lifeless clump of reddish clay lying on the ground came to life that first Friday. God produced irreducible complexity in new living organisms—*biogenesis.* God is the source of life. Job said, *"Remember that you have made me like clay; and will you return me to the dust"* (Job 10:9)?

The word *soul* in Hebrew is *nephesh,* meaning "an animated, breathing, conscious, and living being." The Hebrew word for *spirit* is *ruach,* which means "wind, breath, air, spirit." The spirit and soul of man are immaterial. They are designed to live forever.

VERY GOOD

"God saw everything that he had made,
and indeed it was very good."
Genesis 1:31

A Chronological Pattern on each Day of Creation was similar:

1. Announcement - "God said"
2. Command - "Let there be"
3. Report - "And it was so"
4. Evaluation - "It was good"

GOD IS IN CONTROL

"O LORD God Almighty, who is like you? You are mighty,
O LORD, and your faithfulness surrounds you. You rule over
the raging sea; when its waves mount up, you still them."
Psalm 89:8-9

SOME FACTS YOU WILL LEARN BY READING THIS BOOK

- That this book attempts a comprehensive coverage of a non-moving Earth reality and a Flat Earth reality.
- That the author of this book risks a joust with the Science establishment, with the pseudosciences, and with Christian creationists who accept heliocentrism and round ball globe earthism as true.
- That all of the precise calculations of flight plans for take-off and landing for all aircraft at airports are based on a non-moving Earth.
- That all of the precise calculations for the Space Program are based on a non-moving Earth.
- That all of the precise calculations describing Eclipses are based on a non-moving Earth.
- That all calculations dealing with Navigation, on Satellite movements, on anything which demands accuracy, are formulated on the basis of a stationary Earth.
- That the Bible teaches that the Earth is not moving and can not be moved.
- That rubbery Mathematics have been invented specifically to uphold Copernicanism. 2 + 2 = 5. There is no real evidence that the Earth moves.

- That the roles of Copernicus, Kepler, Galileo, Newton, and Einstein have played in giving this great lie its universal grip on man's "knowledge."
- That the so-called "proofs" of earth's rotation -The Coriolis Effect, Foucault's Pendulum, Geosynchronous Satellites - prove nothing.
- That the LOGIC against a moving Earth is both abundant and overpowering.
- That Zodiac and Parallax factors make the universe at least 25 times smaller than we are told by Darwinian evolutionists.
- That the heliocentric model is a false teaching with no biblical support or scientific evidence.
- That Galileo was flat wrong and the church was right.
- That the geocentric model is the correct teaching with biblical support and scientific evidence.
- That scientific evidence demonstrates through history, philosophy, and mainly through science itself that modern Science has not demonstrated that the earth moves and is not in the center of the universe.
- That observation and experiment indicate that the earth does not move and is in the center of the universe.
- That scientist after scientist admit candidly that "it appears that the earth is standing still" and that " we appear to have a privileged position" (i.e., are at center).
- That the choice is between Copernicus or the Bible.
- That the choice is between philosophy (foolosophy) and vain deceit or true science.
- That the choice is between the Bible and practical astronomy or the Babel of the theoretical and the poetical, Newtonian fiction.
- THAT THE EARTH IS AT CENTER AND IS NOT MOVING.

Verses in the Bible That Describe Earth, Sun & Moon

1. **Earth is a Circle** - The "circle" of Isaiah 40:22 refers to the horizon of the earth, which is perceived as a circle since it can be seen in 360° from most anywhere on a flat earth.

2. **Earth does not Move** ~ Zechariah 1:11; Psalm 104:5; Psalm 93:1; Psalm 96:10; 1 Chronicles 16:30

3. **Earth has Ends** ~ Deuteronomy 28:49; 28:64; 33:17; 1 Samuel 2:10; Job 37:3; 38:13; Psalm 46:9; 48:10; 50:13; 61:2; 65:5; 67:7; 72:8; 98:3; 135:7; Proverbs 17:24; 30:4; Isaiah 5:26; 26:15; 40:28; 41:5; 41:9; 42:10; 43:6; 45:22; 48:20; 49:6; 52:10; Jeremiah 10:13; 16:19; 25:31; 51:16; Micah 5:4; Zechariah 9:10; Acts 13:47

4. **Earth has Corners** ~ Isaiah 11:12; Revelation 7:1

5. **Earth has Pillars** ~ Job 9:6; Psalm 75:3; 1 Samuel 2:8

6. **Earth has a Face** ~ Genesis 1:29; 4:14; 6:1; 6:7; 7:3; 8:9; 11:8; 11:9; 41:56; Exodus 10:5; 10:15; 32:12; 33:16; Numbers 12:3; 22:5; 22:11; Deuteronomy 6:15; 7:6; 1 Samuel 20:15; 1 Kings 13:34; Job 37:12; Psalm 104:30; Jeremiah 8:2;16:4; 25:26; 28:16; Ezekiel 34:6; 38:20; 39:14; Amos 9:6; 9:8; Zechariah 5:3; Luke 21:35; 17:26; Revelation 21:1

7. **See Earth from the Top of a Tall Tree** ~ Daniel 4:11; 4:20

8. **See Earth from the Peak of an exceeding High Mountain** ~ Matthew 4:8

9. **The Sun Moves** ~ Jonah 4:8; Nahum 3:17; Ecclesiastes 1:5; Leviticus 22:7; Deuteronomy 23:11; 24:15; 11:30; 24:13; 16:6; 4:41; 4:47; Joshua 8:29; 1:4; 10:27; 12:1; 1:15; 13:5; 19:12; 19:27; 19:34; 2 Samuel 3:35; 23:4; 2:24; Amos 8:9; Isaiah 60:20; 41:25; 45:6; 49:10; 59:19; Micah 3:6; Ephesians 4:26; Exodus 22:26; 22:3; 17:12; Genesis 15:12; 19:23; 32:31; 15:17; 1 Kings 22:36; 2 Chronicles 18:34; Daniel 6:14; Jeremiah 15:9; Matthew 5:45; James 1:11; Numbers 2:3; 21:11; 34:15; Psalm 19:4-6; 50:1; 113:3; Mark 16:2; Malachi 1:11; Judges 20:43; 8:13; 9:33; 14:18; 19:14.

10. **The Sun is Moved Back 10 Degrees** ~ Isaiah 38:8

11. **The Sun "stood still" and the Moon "stayed"** ~ Joshua 10:12-14

12. **The Sun and the Moon "stood still"** ~ Habakkuk 3:11

13. **Earth was created before the Sun.** DAY 4 of Creation-Sun is Created ~ Genesis 1:16

Questions on Bible Verses

Which came first? The chicken or the egg? The chicken. God doesn't lay eggs. The geocentric non-moving earth came first. Then the Sun.

Is the Earth a Circle? Isaiah 40:22. Is a globe ball earth a sphere or a circle? Is a table with a round top a sphere or a circle? It's a circle.

Does a spherical ball globe have an end? Where is it? Where are the ends of a Beach Ball?

Does a spherical globe have four corners? Where are they? Can you locate four corners on a Beach Ball? Where are they?

Where do the pillars of the earth exist in the NASA CGI images of the earth? The Earth has a face, not a surface. A clock has a face. A map has a face. A person has a face. Can you locate the face on a Beach Ball? Can you locate the face on a globe ball earth? Where would it be? Could you locate a face on a table with a round top? The top of the table is a face. For Earth to have a face it must be a flat plane.

Is it possible on a globe earth to see all the earth from a tall tree that reaches to the heaven? No. On a flat earth, this is possible.

Is it possible on a globe earth to climb the highest mountain and see the kingdoms of the earth? No. This is possible on a flat earth.

Does the Sun move? Yes, according to the Bible. The sun's movement is not a matter of perspective. It is not apparent movement, it is observable. The heliocentric model claims the sun is stationary and is the center of the solar system. There is no evidence for this claim.

"Real eyes realize real lies."

The Bible Says...

The earth is a circle, not a sphere.

The earth is fixed. It does not rotate on an axis or orbit the sun.

The earth has ends. A sphere does not have ends.

The earth has corners. A sphere does not have corners.

The earth has pillars. The CGI images of a global earth from NASA do not show any pillars.

There are no real photos of the Earth from space. They are just photoshop images. NASA gets $50 million a day to show us computer composite images (CGI).

The earth has a face. A spherical surface does not have a face. On a flat earth a face can be established.

Normal movement of the sun is that it follows a path as it orbits above the earth every 24 hours. A sideways eight pattern.

God commanded the sun to stand still for Joshua and once it moved backwards 10 degrees for Hezekiah.

The ends of the earth cannot be established from a spherical surface. The physical laws of nature would allow the ends of the earth to be seen on a flat plane earth.

There is no true formula for spherical trigonometry because, according to non-Euclidean geometry, the three angles of a spherical triangle must together be more than 180°. A triangle can never have more than 180°. Besides, the earth is not a sphere. All the fancy footwork involving invented mathematics is used to measure something that does not exist. Instead of real experiments, spherical trigonometry was used to set up an "intellectual" smoke-screen designed to keep scientists and students from noticing the true and only purpose which was to bury the non-moving Earth taught in the Bible.

Euclid of Alexandria is called the "Father of Geometry." Euclidean geometry has points, lines, and angles. The sum of the interior angles of a triangle is 180o. No more, or less. When Einstein went beyond Euclid, he went too far. Non-Euclid geometry is a fabrication of Einstein's imagination. He could have worked for Walt Disney. You know, non-Euclid Fantasia.

All of a spherical earth could not be seen from any location no matter how high an altitude above sea level.

The Earth is geocentric. It was created the center of the universe on the first day. The sun was created after the earth on the fourth day.

Science and the BIBLE

The BIBLE is the final authority for faith and practice - for belief and behavior, for Orthodoxy and for Orthopraxy. NOT the scientific establishment.

Science and Christianity have an intertwined history. It was only under the Christian worldview that one could expect nature to behave in a way that would make science a reasonable pursuit. It was only in the Christian culture of Europe, and in particular that of Reformation Europe, that science came to fruition.

Creationists everywhere in the Body of Christ must recognize that a geocentric, non-moving Earth is just as vital a biblical doctrine as is the essential Doctrine of Origins. They are fundamentally inseparable!

MONSTROUS LIE

Copernicanism is a monstrous lie, as is evolutionism! To evolutionists, matter is a god. Anyone who upholds that matter is god in the "science" camp has "exchanged the truth about God for a lie and worshiped and served the creature rather than the Creator, who is blessed forever! Amen." (Romans 1:25 ESV). Worshiping matter is what the "science" led Humanist establishment is doing. This is Humanistic folly.

Creator and Sustainer

Jesus, the living Word (Greek: Logos), is the Creator and Sustainer of all that exists - Earth, all life, including mankind, and all the heavenly bodies in the cosmos. The Scriptures are totally clear on this issue: (Colossians 1:16; Ephesians 3:9; Hebrews 1:2, 10; John 1:3,10).

Adam—The First Man

Mitochondrial DNA appears to mutate much faster than expected and raises questions about evolutionary long-age dating. First, it was said that the first man and woman entered the world's history around 1,000,000 years ago, then 200,000 years, then 100,000, then 60,000. But now, Dr. Daniel Criswell says that humanity is just a few thousand years old. You can trust the Word of God.

Human Genome

In the beginning was information. DNA is information. The source of the information is an all-knowing Creator. Yahweh Elohim knows everything about everything. God is both omniscient (all-knowing) and omnipotent (all-power). He does exactly what He wants. Our Father in heaven knows when a sparrow falls to the ground (Matthew 10:29-31). God knows how many hairs are on your head

(Matthew 10:26-31). The average human head has 100,000 hairs. There are 7.6 billion people on earth. That's a big hairy deal. God knows each one personally and completely. God cares about all of humanity.

According to Psalm 139:14-16, all human beings are fearfully and wonderfully made in the image of God. The Psalmist is writing about living organisms and their vital processes in biology. The complete DNA genome, an instruction book for a human, contains about 3 billion bases and about 20,000 genes on 23 pairs of chromosomes. More than 99 percent of those bases are the same in all humankind. Why is the DNA a double helix? Because God always has a witness.

The human body is made in the image of God (1 Corinthians 6:19-20). Our inward parts were intricately woven together, being made in secret by an Intelligent Designer.

Scientific technology has discovered that the human genome is made of deoxyribonucleic acid (DNA), which is a molecule that contains the biological instructions that make each kind unique. DNA, along with the instructions it contains, is passed from adult humans to their offspring during reproduction. The DNA is specific information. A, C, G, and T are the four "letters" of the DNA code; they stand for the chemicals that make up the nucleotide bases of DNA.

The human body is a temple not made with human hands (2 Corinthians 6:16; Revelation 21:3). Humans are made in the Image of God (Genesis 1:26-27; Psalm 139:14-16).

Every single strand of human DNA is marked with the name of Yahweh. There celled bonds hold together the two strands that make up the DNA. It has been discovered that these bonds are located after the tenth nuclear ties, again after the fifth pair, and again six pairs later, and again five pairs later. The tenth (10) letter of the Hebrew alphabet is Yod, the fifth (5) letter is Hey, the sixth (6) letter is vav. Yud-Hey-Vav-Hey spells Yahweh.

The DNA double helix has two types of bonds that are held together with the Hebrews letters Yud-Hey-Vav-Hey. "I AM WHO I AM." The meaning of YHWH abbreviation is "Yahweh" (Hebrew for God). God's name is on every human chromosome. We are made in His image and sealed with the name of our Creator. Every cell in the human body is hallmarked. This gives significant meaning to the concept of being made in the Image of God. The irreducible complexity of each cell is scientific proof that this is the work of an Intelligent Designer, not random chance evolution.

We stand in awe of our great God and all-knowing Creator (Psalm 95:1-7). For this, we praise Yahweh from whom all blessings flow.

The neshamah is a divine spark of YHWH found within mankind. In the beginning, the Creator "breathed upon man and he became a living being." This deposit from above is the gift of a soul. It is what distinguishes us from animal kind, bird kind, and fish kind. There is only one race—the human race. There is only one human kind with different shades of brown skin. There are no human species, only one kind. Inside of each person is the breath of the Creator, known as the soul. In Hebrew, this is called the "neshamah."

That all men are created equal is a self-evident truth. All human life is precious and must be loved and protected. All human beings are endowed by their Creator with certain non-negotiable Rights, that among these are Life, Liberty, and Livability. America has become an Empire of Liberty.

GOD SAID

"For in six days the LORD made heaven and earth, the sea,
and all that in them is, and rested the seventh day:
wherefore the LORD blessed the sabbath day, and hallowed it."
Exodus 20:11

Majestic Creator

"When I look at your heavens, the work of your fingers, the moon and the stars, which you have set in place, what is man that you are mindful of him, and the son of man that you care for him? Yet you have made him a little lower than the heavenly beings and crowned him with glory and honor. You have given him dominion over the works of your hands; you have put all things under his feet."
Psalm 8:3-9 ESV

CULTURAL MANDATE

God blessed Adam and Eve and told them,
"Multiply and fill the earth (family) and subdue it (culture). Be
masters (dominion) over the fish and birds and all the animals."
Genesis 1:28

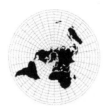

BIG BANG COSMOLOGY

How does anyone know this to be true? Who was there to witness this explosion? Where did the explosive materials come from in the first place? Who set off the explosives? Do explosions cause chaos or create order?

There are big cold and hot spots that lineup around the earth. They are not homogeneous. Why is there a special direction in space? The data shows this to be true. Three different background microwave radiation probes showed that at the center of a moving universe is earth. This was not an error.

We are in the center of the universe. It did not happen by chance. Someone had to put it there. The Intelligent Designer.

Darwinian evolutionary scientists were enraged by the findings. It upset their naturalistic worldview. Their worldview had to displace the earth's special place in the universe, designed for man to live in. We live in a divinely created cosmos.

All of modern cosmology is based on the Copernican principle. Every piece of data that they get in their telescopes has to be filtered through the Copernican principle. That's what the Big Bang theory does, NASA does it, the ESA does it. For the evolutionists, the upsetting thing is that the microwave radiation experiment destroys the Copernican principle. These experiments are not anomalies. Anomaly = irregularity.

What is the motive at work here? Science has become an ideology. Scientism is a religion. Someone bigger than you and I had to create everything that exists. That's what Scientism is afraid of.

31

It takes more faith to believe that nothing produced something than it does to believe "In the beginning God created..."

The earth is in the center of the cosmos. The solar system is cosmically aligned. We are in the center of the universe.

The earth is not moving. Everything else in the cosmos is moving - the sun, the moon, and the stars.

No Observational Science

If you were to take a ride in a hot air balloon or a helicopter, and you went 50,000 feet above sea level, you should be able to see the earth spinning at 1,038 mph below you. That is, if the Earth itself were to be moving. No one has ever observed the ball globe spinning.

- First, the earth is not a ball globe.
- Secondly, the earth does not spin.
- Thirdly, the earth is a flat plane.
- Fourthly, the earth is not moving.

Over 400 years of deception has been exposed. The Bible told the truth all along. The belief that the Earth is rotating on an "axis" and orbiting the sun is the godfather of all deceptions in the world.

If the Earth itself were to be moving: we would be aware of the movement of the ground and the air.

Government sources regarding science know the ball globe earth deception is over, so they are doing everything they can to lead people down new roads of deceit.

OPERATION BLUE BEAM is in full effect. MK ULTRA has been in effect since the 1950s.

NO EXPERIMENT CAN DETECT EARTH'S MOTION

One of the most famous experiments was The Michelson - Morley experiment in 1887. They used light beams to measure if the earth was moving. They found that there was no movement. It showed that the earth is not moving. The experiment: Earth relative to the ether frame.

How do you get out of that? You invent special relativity. This is where Einstein came into the picture. They had to come up with the contraction of mass. They put contraction into a mathematical formula and claimed the opposite of what the experiment proved to be true. In physics, the Lorentz Velocity Transform arises from the idea that 2 + 2 = 5. The transformation of relative velocity is mathematically bogus. The so-called transformations are named after the Dutch physicist Hendrik Lorentz. Lorentz said he had no other explanation to the Michelson-Morley experiment unless he contracted the apparatus. He made it all up. It is a mathematical deception. Otherwise, they would have to accept the proven fact that the earth is standing still in space.

Power Words

Words have meaning. Hebrew words in the OT have descriptive meaning and Greek words in the NT have precise meaning. One of the best ways to know and understand the Bible is to do word studies.

Genesis is not a primitive text written by primitive people. Genesis is not a myth. There is no conflict between Scripture and true science. Evolution is pseudoscience.

Life is impossible without Intelligent Design. And Intelligent Design is impossible without an Intelligent Designer. Genesis 1:1 is the grand design by the Intelligent Designer. It is the most radical verse in all of human history. Radical means root form. God's nature. He is the Creator. God is greater than time, space and number. God's nature is to be good, and with His goodness He blesses us and gives us the freedom to either accept or reject His goodness. That is the foundation for the power to give. God's entire nature is to give blessings. He is not the destroyer. The destroyer is Satan; the devil. In both cases, the accuser. God is the Creator. The only thing He destroys is destruction itself (Satan).

The entire assumption in Genesis 1:1 is that God is the Creator, He is good, and He gives.

Elohim

The one true God who is greater than time, space and number.

Elohim is masculine plural. El = deity. Im = plural. Two or more.

Division: Genesis 1:1 to 2:3.

Genesis 2 is the first covenant.

Universe - One Verse

The universe is finite. There is a beginning but no ending.

The assumption of Genesis: In the beginning God.

Without Form and Void

God began by creating the earth without form and void. No gap. It was confusion without organization. Formless. Unreality. Anything outside of God's reality is unreality. Describes what is not there. Yet. Describes what never existed before it existed. Then, day by day, God worked to shape the formlessness into something beautiful and fill the void with goodness.

We take the text on its own terms with the finest historical criticism we can find and see what the text presents itself. It presents itself as Elohim, the One True Creator. The name given to the Creator is Yahweh. We seek the living God.

We are to accept the Scripture on its face value. The Scriptures are meant to be dug into. We should ask the toughest question about God and the Bible. We look at the text on its own terms. It is consistent and it is simple.

The Heavenly Court

Heaven is God's abode - the Heavenly court with all His heavenly hosts or angels.

YOM = Day

"the" first day. Hebrew word YOM = day. Used with a number = a 24-hour day.

The first words spoken in history are: "Let there be light." Both sound and light.

Three Functions:

- Day One - God created time.
- Day Two - God created weather.
- Day Three - God created food.

YOM + Number

The Hebrew word 'day' [YOM] is a literal 24-hour day. The days are about bringing order.

Text: Genesis 1:1 - 2:3.

Synoptic is doubling back. Genesis 2 is about Day Six.

In the Hebrew language there is no singular word for heaven. It's heavens, plural.

We are all formed from dust = our mortality. Identity.

Adam and Eve were not created mortal. They needed the Tree of Life to stay alive.

Adam had two sides. God took one of them. Woman is the other half of man. Woman makes man complete. Adam married his rib. The two become one flesh. Adam Clay + Eve Rib = completeness.

There is no pre-Adamic race. There is no pre-historic creation. History starts with Adam. The human race started with Adam and Eve. There is only one race - the human race.

God made from one man (Adam) [from one blood] every nation of mankind to live on all the face of the earth. Acts 17:26.

Adam and Eve are historical people. They are real human beings. They were the first human beings on earth. The first Adam was the first man. Eve is the mother of all the living. Thus, we all are related to Adam and Eve.

"Adam called his wife's name Eve, because she was the mother of all the living" (Genesis 3:20).

"Therefore, just as sin came into the world through one man (Adam), and death through sin, and so death spread to all men because all sinned" (Romans 5:12).

In Matthew 19:6 Jesus said that the God who created them (man and woman) from the beginning made them male and female.

Who are the them? Adam and Eve.

When was the beginning? The year of man. Anno Mundi

Anno Mundi (Latin for "in the year of the world;" Hebrew: "to the creation of the world"), abbreviated as AM or A.M., or Year After Creation, is a calendar era based on the biblical accounts of the creation of the world and subsequent history.

The Jewish year starts on Rosh Hashanah, "the Head of the Year," the day when Adam and Eve were created. The amount of years which have elapsed since creation are 5,781.

3760 BC + A.D. 2022 = AD 5782.

> "...In the seventh month, on the first of the month,
> there shall be a sabbath for you, a remembrance
> with shofar blasts, a holy convocation."
> *Leviticus 16:24*

Rosh Hashanah occurs on the first and second days of the Jewish month of Tishri. The Jewish "new year" occurs in Tishri, the seventh month.

To find the corresponding Jewish year for any year on the Gregorian calendar, add 3,760 to the Gregorian number, if it is before Rosh Hashanah.

The Jewish calendar is both lunar and solar; the months are lunar months while the years are solar years.

The Bible is the Final Authority on Geocentrism

There are at least 67 Scriptural references which tell us that it is the Sun and not the Earth that moves. That's a total of 67 verses from the Bible that are geocentric. The number of verses from the Bible which say that the Earth moves is 0.

The fixed position of the earth was obvious to the authors of the Bible. They watched the real motion of the sun, moon, and stars, and observed that the universe revolves around the earth.

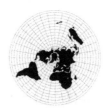

THE BIBLE SAYS THE EARTH IS NOT MOVING

"...Sun, stand still....And the sun stood still, and the moon stopped...."
Joshua 10:12-13 ESV

It is generally agreed that the Bible describes an immovable earth. Here are a few obvious texts:

I Chronicles 16:30: "tremble before him, all the earth; yes, the world is established; it shall never be moved."

Psalm 93:1 ESV: "Yes, the world is established; it shall never be moved"

Job 26:7 ESV: "HE...hangs the Earth on nothing."

Psalm 96:10: "He has fixed the earth firm, immovable ..."

Psalm 104:5 ESV: "He set the earth on its foundation, so it shall never be moved."

Isaiah 45:18: "...who made the earth and fashioned it, and himself fixed it fast..."

Two Bible verses that indicate that the sun orbits the earth:

Ecclesiastes 1:5 ESV: "The sun rises, and the sun goes down, and hastens to the place where it rises."

Joshua 10:13 ESV: "And the sun stood still, and the moon stopped, until the nation took vengeance on their enemies. Is this not written in the Book of Jashar? "The sun stopped in the midst of heaven and did not hurry to set for about whole day."

True Science

The word science comes from the Latin "scientia," meaning knowledge or knowable facts. Webster's Dictionary definition of science is "knowledge attained through study or practice," or "knowledge covering general truths of the operation of general laws, esp. as obtained and tested through scientific method [and] concerned with the physical world."

IGNORANCE
It can be cured!
With knowledge!

Observational Evidence

Observational Evidence is evidence that is based upon physical measurement of some kind.

"Unproven assumptions that are required to explain phenomena that are readily explained without the assumptions constitute false science."
Marshall Hall

The Purpose of Science

Science (not plain science) is at war with the fundamental doctrines of the Christian faith. It should follow then that all true Christians must be at war with Science. They should not sit by complacently while the vain imaginings of the princes of this world are offered as true answers to the most vital questions with which every human being is concerned.

The purpose of science is to produce useful models of reality. Most scientific investigations use some form of the scientific method.

Natural Sciences

Natural Sciences is the study of God's natural world. The different fields of science: Biology, Chemistry, Physics, and Earth Science.

While we are for science, we oppose Science, which is pseudoscience. Science so-called mixes lies with true science or plain science. True science is like good food; pseudoscience is like poison. The two don't mix.

To Kill a Rat

You don't give a rat a bowl of poison to kill it. Rat poison is mixing two things together that don't go together. To kill a rat you mix in a little poison in the food. Rat Poison is 99.9995% Good Food and 0.005% Poison. To get people to believe a lie you mix in a little lie with some truth.

The Motto of False Science

"Don't give up on a good theory just because it isn't true!"

Pseudoscience

Thomas Jefferson said, "We must not be afraid to seek the truth. No matter where it may lead us." Facts are not neutral. All facts are interpreted!

Modern science today is a club. Either you conform to their naturalistic worldview, or you're out. Pseudoscience is made up of statements, beliefs, or practices that claim to be both scientific and factual but are incompatible with the scientific method. In other words, their claim is false. "Real eyes realize real lies."

The Debate

There are only two models: The Geocentric model and the Heliocentric model. The geocentric/heliocentric debate is modern Science versus Scripture. It is also Science versus plain science.

The Bible Stands Like a Rock Undaunted

The Bible is, from Genesis to Revelation, a Creation Bible. The Bible is, from Genesis to Revelation, a geocentric Bible. The Bible is, from Genesis to Revelation, a flat-earth Bible.

Aristotle Believed in a Geocentric Universe

Who was Aristotle? Aristotle (c. 384 BC - c. 322 BC) was an Ancient Greek philosopher and scientist. He is considered one of the greatest thinkers in politics, psychology and ethics. When Aristotle was 17, he enrolled in Plato's Academy. In 338 BC, he began tutoring Alexander the Great.

Aristotle is sometimes called the grandfather of science. He was a student of the great philosopher Plato and in time started his own school, the Lyceum at Athens. He believed in a geocentric universe and that the planets and stars were perfect spheres though the Earth itself was not.

Aristotle argued strongly in favor of this system, on the grounds that if the Earth itself were to be moving:

We would be aware of the movement of the ground or the air.

The position of nearby stars would change in the sky (parallax)

But why do the planets display retrograde motion, moving both forwards and backwards in the sky?

And why did the planets appear brighter at certain times than others?

Desktop Globe

"You shall not make for yourself a carved image, or any likeness
of anything that is in heaven above, or that is in the earth
beneath, or that is in the water under the earth."
Exodus 20:4 ESV

"nor my praise to carved images."
Isaiah 42:8 ESV

The Second Commandment says, "You shall not make for yourself a carved image, or any likeness of anything that is in heaven above." Exodus 20:4 ESV

If you have a desktop model of a spinning globe in your home, office, school classroom, library, business, church, you have a graven image which depicts the earth. Why was this commandment given? Because it indoctrinates without speaking. It depicts a false image of the shape of the earth. The earth is not a globe. The earth is a flat plane.

Plain Science

There is a difference between plain science and Science with a capital S. Science with a capital S is treated like a person or a goddess. The phrase "Science says" is used as though some higher power was speaking.

Plain science gathers knowable facts and puts them into logical order for the purpose of study and application. Its sphere is observation, recording what it sees and hears. Plain science seeks real knowledge, not illusion or imagination.

Science with a Capital S

Men and women who are the products of the American scientific community usually hold religion at arm's length, as do many scientists. They don't want to clutter their well-ordered minds with "mythology." They don't need any religious fantasies interfering with their life.

In these modern days it seems Science with a capital S reigns supreme, a goddess before whom millions of faithful worshipers bow their heads without thinking in childlike trust. Science has become the master word to evoke because it claims to have laid down a firm foundation for a worldview which happily eliminates all those troublesome concepts of sin and guilt, of eternity and a responsibility to an almighty God. If you dare to touch this admired idol with an unfriendly hand, with the purpose of showing its worthlessness, then you must expect to be caught up in the storm of a crushing whirlwind of fanatic vilification.

The hypotheses of evolutionism, heliocentrism, and ball earthism, having all been adopted by naturalistic Scientists generally, are not only used as facts, but insisted upon as such, though to this day no investigations have been able to observe a single case of actual evolution, the earth orbiting the sun, or a globe round earth. Thus plain science is compelled to record untruthfulness as one of the deplorable characteristics of Science.

Science has been steadily at work to overthrow the foundations of faith, and has succeeded in deceiving thousands to their eternal detriment. Disguised as astronomy and geology, Science has jubilantly demonstrated that the first chapters of the Bible contain nothing but myths, which are of no greater historical value than the cosmogony of any pagan culture.

Footstool

"This is what the LORD says: Heaven is my throne, and the earth is my footstool."
Isaiah 66:1 NIV

"or by the earth, for it is his footstool."
Matthew 5:35 ESV

"Heaven is my throne, and the earth is my footstool."
Acts 7:49 ESV

A footstool has four legs or four pillars. From His throne in heaven, God rests His feet on Earth, which is His footstool. How are you mistaking a footstool with a round top for a ball earth? What footstool spins at 1,038 mph?

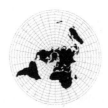

THE CIRCLE
OF THE EARTH

What is the circle of the earth? The "circle" of Isaiah 40:22 refers to the horizon of the earth, which is perceived as a circle since it can be seen in 360o from most anywhere on earth. In Ancient Near Eastern thought, this circle refers to the flat earth disc, not to a sphere.

Young Earth Creationists (YEC) hold the perspective that the "circle of the earth" in Isaiah 40:22 is a reference to a spherical earth. Where is the curvature? A circle is not a sphere. This is a misinterpretation and misunderstanding of this phrase.

One believes things because one has been conditioned to believe them.
Aldous Huxley

YEC have been indoctrinated with Darwinian evolution in the schools they have attended whether it was a Christian school or a non-Christian school or both. They are not aware of their indoctrination. The global earthers have tried to mix both the secular scientific view of today with the perspectives of Scripture that come from a world of Ancient Near Eastern Culture around 3,000 years ago. The OT was written in Hebrew, not English. We must examine the biblical text within the context of background to get an accurate meaning.

Circle Instrument

The Hebrew word (chug) used in Isaiah 40:22 in no way implies a spherical earth. Isaiah 44:13 refers to a "circle instrument," a device used to make a circle, what is called a compass. This "handwriting a circle" in relation to the world refers to the horizon of the earth. Job 26 says "he scribbled a circle on the face of the waters." Job 22:14 says, "he walks on the dome of heaven."

Firmament

The earth was covered by a "firmament," conceived as a large solid upside down bowl or "dome" (Job 22:14; 37:18), in which the stars were placed (Genesis 1:14-20). We live in an enclosed system. When God separated the waters above the expanse He covered the earth with a vault or dome to contain the waters. The sky is blue because water is blue. God lives above the vault. He sits on it and walks on it.

Above the dome is water, which was the source of water for the Flood. The dome has "doors" and "windows" to let the waters above fall to the earth during the Flood of Noah (Genesis 7:11; Isaiah 24:18; Malachi 3:10). Genesis 7:11 says the windows of heaven were opened. On that day when the Flood of Noah started, the fountains of the great deep burst open, and the floodgates of the sky were opened. Plus there was non-stop torrential rain for 40 days and 40 nights. The Flood of Noah was worldwide, not global. Earth is not a globe. The flat-earth was completely flooded. The face of the earth turned back to water again, as in Genesis 1:2. The highest mountains were covered by a depth of 15 cubits of water. A cubit in the Bible is roughly 18 inches. Water covered the earth to a depth of about 8,000 feet.

The waters covered the pre-Flood Earth. Everything changed on earth as a result of the Flood. The Flood was catastrophic to earth's topography and geography and weather. The Bible says that the Flood completely restructured the earth.

The Ancient Near East people, the ancient Hebrews and the Israelis, conceived the world as a large, flat, circular disk anchored in water below (the deep, Proverbs 8:27; Genesis 1:2, 49:25) by pillars or foundations (1 Samuel 2:8; Proverbs 8:29). Between the earth and the deep was Sheol, the place of the dead.

The poetic Ode to Wisdom in Proverbs confirms the ANE view of the world.

"When he established the heavens, I was there,
when he drew a circle on the face of the deep,
When he made firm (firmament) the skies above,
when he established the fountains of the deep.
When he assigned to the sea its limit,
so that the waters might not transgress his command,
when he marked out the foundations of the earth."
Proverbs 8:27-29

This supports the idea of the earth as a flat disc with foundational pillars to allow it to actually "float" on the great deep below the earth.

The Book of Jude

The Epistle of Jude has only one chapter containing 25 verses. The Epistle of Jude was written by the "brother of James," one of four brothers of Jesus. James was the head of the church in Jerusalem; neither James nor Jude were among The Twelve; they didn't believe at first. Until after His resurrection.

The beginning of the Church Age was written about by Luke, called the Acts of the Apostles. The Book of Jude might be called the Acts of the Apostates. Jude is the only book devoted entirely to the great apostasy. "Shall the Son of Man find faith on the Earth?"

Jude is the "vestibule" to the Book of Revelation. It includes the oldest prophecy uttered by a mysterious prophet known as Enoch. Jude 14 says, it was also about these that Enoch, the seventh from Adam, prophesied of the Second Coming of Christ, declared before the flood of Noah. By attributing prophecy to Enoch, Jude confers inspired status upon the book.

"When Enoch had live 65 years, he fathered Methuselah. Enoch walked with God after he fathered Methuselah 300 years and had other sons and daughters. Thus all the days of Enoch were 365 years. Enoch walked with God and he was not, for God took him."
Genesis 5:21-24 ESV

Book of Enoch

A most interesting ancient document describing Hebrew cosmology is 1 Enoch (sometimes called the Ethiopic Book of Enoch). In 1773, the Scottish adventurer James Bruce found complete copies in Ethiopia. Numerous fragments of 1 Enoch were found among the Dead Sea Scrolls at Qumran.

The Enochian cosmology is the same flat-earth cosmology derived from the canonical books. "Book of Enoch" in The Apocrypha and Pseudepigrapha of the Old Testament in English.

1 Enoch influenced Christian eschatology, and it should be necessary reading for anyone trying to understand Hebrew religious thought at the dawn of the Christian era. From their geographical and historical context, one would expect the ancient Hebrews to have a flat-earth cosmology. From the very beginning, orthodox Christians have been flat-earthers, arguing that to believe otherwise is to deny the literal truth of the Bible. The flat-earth implications of the Bible were rediscovered and popularized by English-speaking Christians in the mid-19th century. Liberal scriptural scholars later derived the same view.

Enoch influenced Matthew, Luke, John, Acts, Romans, and several other New Testament books. The punishment of the fallen angels described in 2 Peter seems to come directly from 1 Enoch, as does much of the imagery (or even wording) in Revelation. The Epistle of Jude contains evidence of its influence when it condemns the "enemies of religion" as follows:

> "I saw the Lord come with his myriads of angels, to bring all men
> to judgment and to convict all the godless of all the godless
> deeds they had committed, and of all the defiant words
> which godless sinners had spoken against him."
> *Jude 14-15*

Foundations

There are numerous Old Testament verses referring to the earth's foundations. Foundations are hard to explain because they can't be seen. Foundations are covered by geocentricity. No one would argue for a flat-earth solely on the basis of "foundations" quotes. Here are five quotes:

"Then the channels of the earth were seen;
the foundations of the world were laid bare, at the rebuke
of the LORD, at the blast of the breath of his nostrils."
2 Samuel 22:16 ESV

"Where were you when I laid the foundations of the earth?
Tell me, if you have understanding."
Job 38:4 ESV

"Then the channels of the sea were seen,
and the foundations of the world were laid bare."
Psalm 18:15 ESV

"When he assigned to the sea its limit, so that
the waters might not transgress his command,
when he marked out the foundations of the earth."
Proverbs 8:29 ESV

"For the windows of heaven are opened,
and the foundations of the earth tremble."
Isaiah 24:18b ESV

Cosmology - The Flat-Earth Model

In the English-speaking world, flat-earthism is and always has been entirely based on the Bible. The Bible describes an immovable earth.

THE FLAT-EARTH VIEW IS GEOCENTRIC

What is the flat-earth model? The earth is a flat disk, with the North Pole at its center. There is no south pole. The earth is bounded by a 200 feet high "Ice Wall" called Antarctica. The ice wall keeps all the oceans water contained on earth.

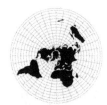

ASTRONOMY—THE GEOCENTRIC MODEL

The earth is the center of the cosmos. The Sun, the Moon, and the stars revolve around the Earth. They are not embedded in the sky. Nor do not they get their rotating motion from a spinning earth.

The teaching of Geocentricity in Western thought can be traced back to Aristotle (384-322 B.C.). Aristotle argued that the reason why all bodies fall to the ground is because they seek their natural place at the center of the universe, or the earth. Geocentricism was generally accepted by scientists before Christ until Copernicus introduced his theory in AD 1543.

For the first 1,500 years of church history both the church and science held to the Geocentric Theory of Cosmology. A Geocentric model was first formalized by Ptolemy, the famous Greek astronomer who lived in Alexandria around AD 130.

The Earth Stands Fast

We live on a non-moving Earth. The earth is fixed. The earth is suspended in space by the power of electromagnetic force between the North Pole and the North Star-Polaris. Both the North Pole and the North Star are powerful opposing magnets. Both are fixed or non-moving. There is repulsion between the two magnetic dipoles which keeps the earth hanging or suspended on nothing. The Earth hangs on nothing and is not spinning or orbiting.

Earth Not Tilted On an Axis

Earth does not "wobble" on an axis. If the Earth wobbled, we certainly would feel it. Run for your bunker, brother. Darwinian evolution claims the global Earth model has an axial tilt of 23.4° off of true North. This is pseudoscience. An axial tilt of 23.4° places the North Pole off vertical. That the Earth's axis is off vertical is not a fact of true science. God did not create a tilted Earth. He created it vertical. Straight up and down. North is North. Earth's polar axis is not at a 66.6° angle. That's Satanism. There is no rotation axis. Earth is perpendicular, not on an axial tilt. North celestial pole is due North, not tilted on an axis. Darwinian evolution claims that if the earth were not tilted on its axis, there would be no seasons. This is absolutely false. There are four seasons because Yahweh created them and told us He did. The annual calendar is divided into four seasons. Each season is three months and follows the same order: Spring, Summer, Fall, and Winter.

> "And God said, "Let there be lights in the expanse
> of the heavens to separate the day from the night.
> And let them be for signs and for seasons,
> and for days and years."
> *Genesis 1:14 ESV*

> "While the earth remains, seedtime and harvest, cold and heat,
> summer and winter, day and night, shall not cease."
> *Genesis 8:22 ESV*

Earth does not orbit the Sun at 67,000 mph. There is no empirical evidence to show this to be true. Information has not been obtained through observation, documentation, patterns or through experiment. The pseudoscientists who hold to heliocentrism just made it up. Pseudoscientists seek falsifications. Earth is not a planet. The word planet means wanderer. Earth does not wander in space. Earth is fixed; immovable; motionless.

Earth Cannot Be Moved

> "Yahweh reigns, He is clothed with majesty; Yahweh
> has clothed and girded Himself with strength; Indeed,
> the world is firmly established, it will not be moved."
> *Psalm 93:1*

Coriolis Effect

Frenchman, mathematician, and engineer, Gustave Coriolis (1792-1843) described the Coriolis force as "an effect of motion on a rotating body."

What is the Coriolis Effect? The Coriolis Effect is a demonstrable reality which results when something is in motion over a rotating base.

The use of this concept to claim proof for the Earth ís rotation is a hoax of a high order.

This does not prove the Earth is moving!

Long range missiles are based on a non-rotating Earth. The equations and physics used by NASA to launch satellites are identical to the equations derived from a geocentric universe. The same is true of the equations and physics used to guide missiles or jets or artillery shells. If missiles or jets or artillery shells were corrected in flight for a rotating Earth, they would never hit their targets or get to the airport. Why? Because the Earth is not rotating.

The evidence for a non-moving Earth is all around us all the time! When a missile is fired longitudinally where a geostationary (non-moving) satellite can track it the missile goes straight to its destination while the Earth stands perfectly still beneath while it is sailing in the air. Fire a long-range cannon due north or south with a trajectory that will keep it in the air as long as possible and see if the target moved several miles when the shell hits.

The Coriolis Effect is a demonstrable reality which results when something is in motion over a rotating base. But applying this demonstrable reality to the Earth which has never been shown to be moving is a contra-scientific deception! The only value of the Coriolis Effect is that - with a controlled cannon or missile experiment - it can be used to prove that the Earth is not turning.

The Bible and Science

The Bible speaks of the Earth's free float in space. Job 26:7 says God hangs the earth on nothing. Science discovered that fact in 1650. Everything we see is composed of things that we cannot see - invisible atoms. Hebrews 11:3 tells us that the "things which are seen were not made of things which do appear."

Steady-state theory. No! What is steady-state theory? In cosmology, a view that the universe is always expanding but maintaining a constant average density, with matter being continuously created to form new stars and galaxies at the same rate. This is preposterous. Only Elohim can create matter and stars. The universe has not expanded since the day God completed His work of creation. It's vast, but the same size. Everything God intended to create has been created. The realm of embodied existence has been completed, and everything placed in that realm has filled it up. See: Genesis 2:1.

Big Bang Cosmology out of nothing? No.

There's no scientific revelation. The living God, a Spirit being, has revealed Himself to man in the world. He is not hidden.

"The heavens declare the glory of God, and the sky above proclaims his handiwork."
Psalm 19:1

"By faith we understand that the universe was created by the word of God, so that what is seen was not made out of things that are visible"
Hebrews 11:3

THE BIG BANG
IS A THEORY

God did it. Creation was supernatural, not natural.

Evolution is a mass deception. Evolution is a lie. Evolutionists lie to promote and to protect the lie of evolution. The Big Bang theory predicts there was an explosion 13.7 billion years ago. The explosion had to come out equal on all sides of the sphere. Called homogeneous. But it is not homogeneous. The hot spots form an X in the universe with earth in the middle. The two lines in the X represent hot and cold spots with earth at the center of the X.

False Presumptions and Wrong Assumptions

We need to shed the heavy baggage of our school indoctrination and subsequent misconceptions of what the Bible actually says about origins. The good news is that 20th century science has vindicated the biblical perspectives of reality portrayed in the Bible. We know the universe is infinite, not finite. That was a shocking discovery to secular scientists. We now know that the nature of time is not what Einstein's theory of general relativity claimed. Massive objects do no warp the fabric of space-time, a distortion that manifests as gravity.

Try to set aside the presumptions we've all been conditioned with from our schooling and the culture at large. We have been programmed with stuff that just is not true.

The way to avoid truth is to condemn before investigation. You must not condemn the geocentric model and the flat-plane earth model before investigation. If you say, "Don't confuse me with the facts, my mind is already made up!" Then you have been indoctrinated with Darwinian evolution and don't even realize it. Indoctrination gets a grip on the mind and won't let go. The only thing that can release the grip is truth. The truth will set you free (John 8:32).

Age of the Earth

The question is not what we believe about the age of the earth, the question is what we believe about the authority of God's Word.

> "All scripture is God-breathed!"
> *2 Timothy 3:16*

Heat always flows from hot bodies to cold bodies. If the universe is infinitely old, then the temperature throughout the universe would be uniform. The Earth is not cold, therefore, it is not infinitely old.

The Big Bang is an imaginary idea: First there was nothing, and then it exploded. That's ex nihilo.

The universe had a beginning - Genesis 1:1.

Usher's Classic Dates

James Usher (1581-1656) was Archbishop of the Church in Ireland. He believed the Word of God and was a prolific scholar who published a chronology that purported to establish the time and date of creation based on the biblical record as 4004 BC, according to the Julian calendar. His findings were based on accurate and correct interruptions of the Bible documented throughout the OT. From his early schools days he excelled in history, and from the time he was 20 for the next two decades he read every history book he could get his hands on. He excelled in church history and prepared several large authoritative works dealing with the Irish and English churches from the times of the apostles. Usher first made the assumption that the Bible was the only reliable source document of chronological information for the time periods covered in the Bible. He chose the death of Nebuchadnezzar as a reliable date to anchor all the earlier biblical dates to. Working backward from that date he ended up with his classic date for creation in 4004 BC.

Archbishop James Usher and Dr. John Lightfoot (both in the 17th century) went through a careful study of the genealogists and concluded that the creation of the cosmos occurred in 4004 BC. Archbishop James Usher set the Date for Creation: October 23, 4004 B.C.

More recent scholars have gone through Usher's dates and have some minor discrepancies, but not much, with Usher's dates. Those scholars are: William Henry Green and B.B. Warfield, Princeton, in the 19th century. E.W. Faulstich, a computer analysis, 1979. and Walter T. Brown, 1995.

Biblical scholars today do not depart far from Usher's dates that are included in many study Bibles.

In Six Days: Why Fifty Scientists Choose to Believe in Creation. In this book are the testimonies of 50 men and women holding doctorates in a wide range of scientific fields who have been convicted by the evidence to believe in a literal six-day creation.

All 50 of these scientists, through faith and scientific fact, have come to the conclusion that God's Word is true and everything had its origin not so very long ago, in the beginning, In Six Days. These 50 scientists have gone on record believing the six days perception of Genesis is the valid perception scientifically. They have scientific reasons for believing that.

Our Finite Beginning

Creation did not start with The Big Bang ex nihilo (Latin: out of nothing, from nothing).

Creation started when God spoke. Ex Logos.

Young-Earth Creation (YEC)

Young-earth creationism is historic Christian orthodoxy. The writers of Scripture believed that Genesis teaches a literal six-day creation about 6,000 years ago.

Does the age of the earth matter? Millions of years or 6,000 years? Darwinian evolution or God spoke creation? Many competing views have produced confusion and led many Christians to conclude that they just don't know and they don't care.

Young-earth creationists believe that the days of creation in Genesis were six literal (24-hour) days, which occurred around 6,000 years ago. They believe the surface of the earth was radically rearranged by Noah's Flood. Creationists believe that the Flood was worldwide and catastrophic. The Flood was responsible for most of the rock layers and fossils buried in rock layers all over the earth.

Genesis is literal history about origins. It is not fiction, parable or mythology. It is literal history written by Moses.

The meaning of the Hebrew word yom in the OT is a literal day when used with a number (day one, second day, etc.) and with evening and morning.

The darkness upon the face of the deep in Genesis 1:2 was an unusual darkness; a heavy darkness that can be felt. The Plague of Darkness in Exodus 10:21 was also an unusual darkness; a heavy darkness that could be felt. The "deep" is the abyss, the home of demons and evil spirits. This is spooky.

When were the angels created? In the beginning. Angels witnessed "the foundation of the earth" in Job 38:4-7. All the angels shouted for joy as they witnessed creation.

God created supernaturally and instantly. Everything was fully formed and fully functioning. All plants, animals, birds, fish, and humans were mature adults ready to reproduce naturally "after their kinds." God spoke "let there be . . . ," and it was so. No wait time for things to come into existence. No evolving. He spoke, and things happened immediately. This included light travel. See Psalms 33:6-9.

God created dinosaurs on Day Six with all the other land animals. Genesis 1:21, 25 ("great sea creatures" and "beasts of the earth"). Dinosaurs did not exist millions of years ago. T-Rex was a herbivore in the garden. The name dinosaur comes from two Greek words deinos ("terrible" or "fearfully great") and sauros ("reptile" or "lizard"). Dinosaur = terrible lizard.

Noah took two dinosaurs onto the ark. Youngins. Before the Flood of Noah, everything grew larger and lived longer because there was 100% air pressure and 100% oxygen level, like a hyperbaric oxygen chamber. Dinosaurs have a small lung capacity. After the flood, the air pressure and oxygen level dropped on earth. After the flood, they reproduced after their kind, but they could not get enough oxygen to run and escape from their enemies. Most died off, but some dinosaurs still exist on earth today. A dinosaur called Mokele-mbembe lives in the Congo River Basin. https://drdino.com/dinosaur-adventure-land/

Dinosaur (terrible lizard)

Keep in mind: Until 1848, the word dinosaur was not in the English lexicon. Biblical names like dragon, leviathan, behemoth, fiery flying serpents, and cockatrice were used to describe the giant fossils and strange creatures that were being discovered. Dragons and dinosaurs were seen as "common" animals.

English anatomist Richard Owen proposed the formal term Dinosauria in 1842. Noah took two dinosaurs onto the ark, male and female. There is biblical evidence that dinosaurs roamed the earth after the flood. Job 41:1 mentions a great sea creature. Isaiah 27:1 refers to a great serpent in the sea. Job 40:15-24 describes an enormous creature called a Behemoth. The Flood of Noah destroyed most of the dinosaurs on earth. Today we see evidence of dinosaur bones and remains buried and fossilized in rock layers.

The order of creation in Genesis 1 contradicts the order of events in the evolutionary Big Bang theory. Darwinian evolution has everything backwards.

In the middle of the Ten Commandments, Exodus 20:11 says God created everything in six days. These are 6/24 hour days. God doesn't lie. These verses rule the day-age view out and the gap theory. Any attempt to add millions of years before the beginning is not based on the Bible. God made nothing before these first six days. God gave a reason for six-day creation. The reason: work six days, rest on the seventh day, a reason for Sabbath-keeping. The days of the Jewish work-week are the same as the days of Creation Week. After 6,000 years, people all over the world still follow this weekly pattern: six and one = seven.

Jesus referred to Adam and Eve, Cain and Abel, Noah and the Flood, and Sodom and Gomorrah. He took the events recorded in Genesis as literal history. Jesus said that man was created at the beginning of creation, which confirms the young-earth creationist view. See Mark 10:6, 13:9 and Luke 11:50-51. The miracles of Jesus confirm the young-earth view. When Jesus spoke, miracles happened. His words brought an immediate, instantaneous result, just as when God spoke in Creation Week.

The Bible teaches that no animals or humans died before the Fall of Adam and Eve. Therefore, the geological record of rock layers and fossils could not be millions of years before the Fall. To the evolutionists, fossils represent death, not life. They represent millions of years of history. Around the world there is evidence of violent carnage in fossil graveyards which contain millions of former living creatures compacted in high concentrations.

The Flood of Noah was not global because the earth is a flat plane. Water does not bend or curve or hang suspended perpendicular in oceans at a steep angle. A cheer for gravity: "Go gravity, you can do it." What holds the millions of gallons of water in the oceans in its place on a ball globe? Not gravity. Impossible. Water flows downward and seeks its own level. We say 'sea level' because, see, the sea is level, not curved at eight inches per mile. Utterly ludicrous. The Flood of Noah was a worldwide catastrophic flood responsible for producing most of the geological record of rock layers and fossils buried in the rock layers. The Flood was not a local flood in Mesopotamia.

Moses compiled the Book of Genesis. Adam wrote Genesis 5. Shem wrote Genesis 11.

The genealogies recorded in Genesis 5 and 11 give the years from the first man, Adam to Abraham, who lived about 2000 BC. This sets the date of creation at approximately 6,000 years ago or 4004 BC, according to Usher's date.

The biblical literature shows the Tree of Life with four rivers with honey, oil, milk and wine flowing down into Eden.

According to Genesis 1:29-30, man, animals, and birds were originally vegetarian. Plants are not called "living creatures" (Hebrew: nephesh chayyah), as people, land animals, birds and sea creatures are called. Plant "death" is not the same as animal or human death. God called the creation "good." When He completed His creation on Day Six, after He made the woman, He called everything "very good."

"Thus the heaven and earth were completed in all their vast array or all the host of them." Genesis 2:1 states that creation was perfected and completed in the space of six days. Everything God thought of, He created, perfected, and completed. He forgot nothing. The Intelligent Designer knows everything about everything.

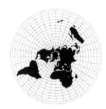

NATIONAL AERONAUTICS & SPACE ADMINISTRATION

In Hebrew, NASA literally translates "to deceive." Why does NASA have a red snake tongue in their logo? Deception! As the Indian Chief said to the Lone Ranger, "Him speak with forked-tongue."

NASA Dreamers and Schemers

Did you know that the ultimate goal of NASA's exoplanet program is to find unmistakable signs of current life on a planet beyond Earth? NASA is searching for life among the stars. Make no mistake, there is no life on any planet beyond Earth, except in Heaven. Only Earth is hospitable to life. No planet has ever at any time been hospitable to life. There is no Man in the Moon! There are no red aliens running around on the red Martian soil of Mars! The NASA dreamers and schemers are full of methane gas.

The Origin of Astrology

The Bible reveals that God created and placed the heavenly bodies. In the Book of Job, God is identified as the Author of the constellations and of individual stars. Job 9:9 tells us, "He is the Maker of the Bear and Orion, the Pleiades and the constellations of the south." See Job 26:13 and 38:31-33.

The stars were to be used for "signs" and for "seasons" (Genesis 1:14). God's Word forbids the practice of astrology (Isaiah 47:12-14), which has long been associated with evolutionary pantheism and occultism.

A sign is a beacon that points toward something else. Its purpose is to help one locate or identify. The 12 signs of the zodiac and their 36 "decans" have been corrupted over the centuries of time into the pagan system of astrology. Satan has no creative ability, so this liar resorts to counterfeiting. He perverted the reason for the stars, tempting man to look to them for purpose and direction in life. Based on an astrological chart of demonic power and deception, he uses the system of signs and seasons to divert man's attention away from God.

Evidence indicates that the heavenly bodies connected with the stars were fashioned to tell a message about the Creator's plans for mankind. The "Gospel in the stars" was on display every night with the important message: God Himself became incarnate in human flesh.

Since we now have God's written Word, this ancient message written in the stars is no longer needed (Hebrews 1:1-2).

The heavens are still declaring the glory of God (Psalm 19:1), and the Lord Jesus Christ is the brightness of His glory (Hebrews 1:3). See: 2 Corinthians 4:6.

Star Worship

When the canopy collapsed at the time of the Flood, the sun and moon became clearly visible for the first time. The first form of religious rebellion against Yahweh after the Flood centered on astrology and the Tower of Babel (Genesis 11).

Some creationists believe the canopy was translucent which allowed the stars, the sun, the moon and the planets to be visible to the naked eye. Could be.

The collapse of the canopy explains the sudden burst of sun worshipers recorded throughout the world. Within 150 years after the Flood, the entire human race, which spoke one language, was engrossed in astrology and sun worship. The Triune God came down and put an end to the Tower of Babel project by creating new languages (Genesis 11:7).

Astrology - Heliocentric Model

The Greek word "helios" means "sun." The heliocentric model claims that the sun is at the center of the solar system. A heliocentric system is one in which the planets revolve around a fixed sun. Thus Mercury, Venus, the Earth, Mars, Jupiter and Saturn all revolve around the sun. The moon is the only celestial sphere in this system which revolves around the earth, and, together with it, around the sun.

Evolutionists think there is nothing unusual about Earth. It's an average rock spinning mindlessly around a common star in a run-of-the-mill galaxy. The late Carl Sagan said, "a lonely speck in the great enveloping cosmic dark." He was dead wrong.

There's nothing ordinary about the Milky Way galaxy. It's in a special place in the universe. Earth occupies a privileged position on the edge of the Milky Way galaxy, which points to a Designer for Earth.

The heliocentric astronomical model holds that the Earth and planets revolve around a stationary Sun at the center of the Solar System. It was not until the 16th century that a fully predictive mathematical model of a heliocentric system was presented, by the Renaissance mathematician, astronomer, and Catholic cleric Nicolaus Copernicus of Poland, leading to the Copernican Revolution.

The Heliocentric theory was first proposed by Nicolaus Copernicus. Copernicus was a Polish astronomer. He first published the heliocentric system in his book: "On the revolutions of the heavenly bodies," which appeared in 1543. Copernicus died the same year his book was published.

In 1539, the Protestant Reformer Martin Luther denounced the new theory - heliocentrism. The Catholic Church disregarded Copernicus' book until 1616, when it was included in the "Index:" A list of prohibited books.

There were objections to the theory that were not religious in nature. Most astronomers and natural philosophers of that period claimed that Copernicus' theory was scientifically implausible and raised many counter claims.

The evidence for heliocentrism is alleged. Consider the lame heliocentric explanation: We are in an atmospheric "envelope" that rotates in perfect synchronization with the earth. Does that mean the air speed has to adjust perfectly to the ground speed every inch you go from the equator's 1,000 MPH + to zero MPH at the poles? God did not use hooks and loops (Velcro) to attach the clouds to earth's atmosphere. That is not realistic. In fact, it's impossible. This is pseudoscience that does not match observation or experience.

A cloud is made of water drops or ice crystals floating in the sky. Clouds gather and scatter. As air rises it cools and decreases pressure, spreading out. Water vapor condenses to form a cloud. New cloud drops are always forming in the place where clouds are in the sky. Dark gray clouds are a sure sign of rain. White, puffy clouds are a sign of a bright and pleasant day ahead. Rain or shine, today is a gift, that's why it's called the present.

Clouds move because the wind is carrying the parcel of cloudy air along. No wind, no cloud movement. Wind blows at all levels of the atmosphere from the ground up to higher levels. Higher than a jumbo jet can fly. Air is pushed up so the front of the cloud appears stationary. It's getting bigger on the upside. Clouds both cool down and warm up the temperatures on earth. Clouds block light and heat from the sun, making earth's temperature cooler. Airplanes fly through clouds and all they get is wet.

The ascension of Jesus was on a cloud elevator (Acts 1:9-11). If the earth was actually spinning at 1,038 mph that historic day, then Jesus would still be looking for a cloud to receive Him. Spinning at 1,038 mph would produce high winds, and no cloud elevator.

If the earth is actually spinning at 1,038 mph on an axis, then who is oiling the axis so it does not overheat and catch on fire? An angel?

Ladies and gentleman, the earth is not spinning on its axis at 1,038 mph. No spin, no axis. The earth is fixed.

The Big Bang Cosmology

Are we winners in a giant cosmic lottery?

Evolution is not the only thing we are being lied to about. The Earth under our feet was molded into a spinning ball that is a by-product of the Big Bang, which was a theory that was introduced to science in 1931. Secular scientists say the Big Bang started with nothing, and then exploded. In order for evolution to work, the Big Bang that was somehow pinpointed to 4.54 billion years ago has to be true. In the big bang cosmology, the Earth is a sphere orbiting around the sun. The issue is that the motion of the Earth has never been detected.

Adolph Hitler

"If you tell a lie long enough, loud enough and often enough,
the people will believe it."
The Third Reich at War p. 38

"People are more likely to believe a big lie than a small one."

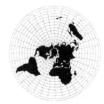

EVOLUTION IS A BIG LIE

Evolution is not science. Evolution is a bankrupt theory. An unproven theory. A theory that is not provable. Evolution violates the 1st and 2nd laws of thermodynamics. This unproven scheme is merely a hypothesis (a proposal; a guess). The theory of evolution cannot be proven because it is impossible for nothing to create something ex nihilo. Evolution is a BIG lie. Evolution is pseudoscience verses science. It is not science verses religion. The Creation account is not religion just because it's in the Bible. The Creation account is literal history of the way the world began.

Darwin's Favored Races

Charles Darwin was a racist. His first book's full original title was On the Origin of Species by Means of Natural Selection, or the Preservation of Favoured Races in the Struggle for Life.

Darwin's second book was about evolutionary theory. The Descent of Man, and Selection in Relation to Sex, was published in 1871. Not a good read. Darwin proves that he is a racist and discriminatory. His beliefs and practices follow from his theories. Darwin addressed human evolution and race. He applied his theories of natural selection to humans and introduced the idea of sexual selection. His white supremacy jumps off the pages. Darwin described some people groups as "savages." He considers every population that is not white and European to be savage. He said that the highest race and the lowest savages are different in "moral disposition and in intellect." His perspective on non-European races is unbelievably prejudiced and absurd. This book was worse than his first book. Ditch Darwin and his theories.

Evolution is based on two faulty assumptions:
1. mutations make something new
2. natural selection makes the new survive and takes over the population

We need to think critically. Dinosaurs, mammals, and birds came into existence during creation week around 6,000 years ago, not millions of years ago. Do you think humans are still evolving? Is there any monkey business in your family tree? Are you a descendant of the faulty reconstruction of the Neanderthal skeleton from La Chapelle-aux-Saints or the Piltdown Man fraud or the old Java Man? Is your father's father's father a monkey's uncle? Humans are descendants of Adam and Eve, not trousered apes.

Adam and Eve were created in the image (spiritual) and likeness (physical) of God (Genesis 1:26). They were created fully grown mature adults. No evolving going on.

Indoctrination vs Education

There is a stark difference between indoctrination and education. Adolf Hitler said, "Let me control the textbooks and I will control the state..." In the video, Let My Children Go, author Caryl Matritiano states, "75% of all children raised in Christian homes who attend public schools will reject the Christian faith by their first year of college. Professor Louis Bounoure, Director of Strasbourg Zoological Museum said, "Evolution is a fairy tale for grownups. The theory has helped nothing in the progress of science. It is useless." Dr. T.N. Tahmisian, Atomic Energy Commission, USA, said, "Scientists who go about teaching that evolution is a fact of life are great con men, and the story they are telling maybe the greatest hoax ever. In explaining evolution we do not have one iota of fact."

Sir Arthur Keith wrote the forward to the 100th anniversary edition of Darwin's book, Origin of Species in 1959. He said, "Evolution is unproved and unprovable. We believe it only because the only alternative is special creation, and that is unthinkable."

We have inherited the atheistic legacy of the contrarians (contrary position) Copernicus, Kepler, Galileo, Darwin and Marx for the truth of God's Word and true science.

What we need in our schools, colleges, universities, and seminaries is evidence based education. There is no evidence for Darwinian evolution, heliocentrism, or a spherical earth that spins. These ideas can be disproven. Young people are being taught pagan fallacies and evolutionary myths that lead to relativism, which is a denial of absolutes. The denial of absolutes causes young people to do what is right in their own eyes. Substituting bad for good and wrong for right is the epitome of ignorance.

Scientists Who Rejected Geocentrism

Three centuries before Christ, Aristarchus calculations were wrong. He held that the sun and moon were at the center of the universe. He rejected geocentrism in favor of heliocentrism, that the sun is the center of the cosmos.

The views of Aristotle were correct. He embraced geocentrism, that the earth is the center of the cosmos. This view held sway for almost two more millennia.

Copernicus abandoned the geocentric model held by Ptolemy in favor of the heliocentric model held by Aristarchus. Copernicus was wrong, the Scriptures are right. The Copernican Revolution challenged the biblical view of geocentrism. Not until Kepler in 1620 did false science data overcome the scientific evidence.

The Witchcraft Connection

Ephesians 6:12 says we wrestle against Satan and his demons. Heliocentrism is a Satanically inspired deception capable of fooling the whole world. In Kepler's day people from all walks of life believed in Satanism, witchcraft, demon activity, black magic, and occult practice. Modern "science" now labels it as "superstition."

Tycho Brahe was known for his excellent precision. Brahe held to the geocentric model. Johannes Kepler sought out Tycho Brahe. He joined him as a junior partner in astronomical research. He signed a two year contract. Kepler held to the heliocentric model. Brahe could not accept the heliocentric model. He pleaded with Kepler not to use his information to support Copernicanism.

Forty-nine charges of witchcraft were brought against Johannes Kepler's mother, Katherine. It landed her in jail. She stood trial as a witch. She was finally acquitted. Kepler's mother was raised by a female relative who was executed for practicing witchcraft. Kepler was reared in an obviously anti-Christian atmosphere.

Tycho died in 1601 at age 54. He was healthy, but ate something, got sick, stayed sick for a couple weeks, and up and died. Poisoned? On his deathbed, Tycho pleaded with Kepler not to use his records to support Copernicanism. Tycho knew about Kepler's Copernican bias. The Roman Church had required Kepler to remove his original opening chapter in his manuscript entitled Cosmic Mystery in 1597. In it, Kepler refuted the biblical quotations that were used to discredit the Copernican theory.

Galileo struggled with the Roman Church. Galileo believed in the heliocentric model, but had no evidence. The Roman Church believed in geocentrism based on the repository of Truth found in the Scripture. Galileo was wrong. The church was right!

On the one hand, early in the 17th century the Roman Church officially called Galileo to stand trial and forced him to recant his attempts to promote Copernicanism, or until he could come up with some evidence. On the other hand, the Roman Church today wants to erase the image of having stood against what the whole world now sees as the truth of Copernicanism and the house arrest of Galileo. The encyclopedia says Galileo invented the telescope. He did not.

Neither Copernicus, Galileo, Kepler, Newton, or Einstein, ever proved the Earth to be moving. None of them.

When Galileo was young he shared his opinions about Copernicanism in a favorable light with the younger Kepler. Kepler became Tycho Brahe's assistant. Brahe's reputation was great. The clarity of his geocentric model stood firmly against Copernicanism. Tycho Brahe stood in the way of "progress" as far as Galileo and Kepler saw it. Both Galileo and Kepler shared a desire to overthrow the biblical system with its non-moving Earth. Neither one of them ever produced any evidence to back up their belief in Copernicanism. Both of them tried to fool church officials about their intentions, but never succeeded.

What about the witchcraft connection in Kepler's life? Are the roots of heliocentrism's success and how such an idea with no foundation could deceive the whole world planted in the soil of Satan worship? John 10:10 says: "The thief comes only to steal and kill and destroy." The thief in this case is the deceptive leaders of heliocentrism.

Nicolaus Copernicus

Nicolaus Copernicus (1473-1543) was a Polish astronomer (real name Mikolaj Kopernik). In his book, On The Revolutions Of The Celestial Spheres, he claimed that Earth moved. Copernicus basically "borrowed" the concept of heliocentrism from Aristarchus and worked it over and put his own name on it. The name Copernicus alone has become virtually synonymous with the hypothesis that the earth revolves daily on an axis and orbits the sun annually. The heliocentric system is commonly referred to as the Copernican system. Aristarchus is all but forgotten.

Copernicus proved nothing, but nevertheless set off what has been called "The Copernican Revolution." The foundations or premises are always unproved; no proof is ever attempted; the necessity for it is denied; it is considered sufficient that the assumptions will seem to explain the phenomena selected. Copernicus admitted, "It is not necessary that hypotheses should be true, or even probable; it is sufficient that they lead to results of calculation which agree with calculations." How arrogant and stupid can you get? The hypotheses of the terrestrial motion was nothing but an hypotheses, valuable only so far as it explained phenomena, and not considered with reference to absolute truth or falsehood.

The revolution was against the authority of Scripture, and still is. Are we going to believe secular science or the Bible?

God plainly says the sun goes around the Earth. Man says the Earth goes around the sun. It was Copernicus who kicked off the modern revolt against what the Bible says. Kepler, Galileo, Einstein and a herd of others after Copernicus have planted his revolutionary flag in every school and library in the world, and some churches as well. The pseudoscience establishment has exalted his theory above Scripture and over what the Bible teaches on moral and ethical issues.

The deceptions of heliocentricity and evolutionism are like two great flood gates that contain a hidden lake full of Satan's deceptions of all kinds. These two gates need to be exposed and ultimately destroyed.

A half century after Copernicus, Galileo - with telescope in hand - claimed he corroborated the heliocentric model. The Roman churchmen were right. In 1633, the Inquisition of the Roman Catholic Church forced Galileo Galilei to recant his theory that the Earth moves around the Sun. Galileo was ordered to turn himself into the Church court to begin trial for holding the belief that the earth revolves around the sun. The Catholic Church found him guilty of heresy based of the teachings of the Bible. The Church was not mistaken. Galileo was wrong. Galileo used pseudoscience to claim that his understanding of moving planets was correct. There is a big problem with seeing the Galileo story as a narrative of the Church denying science. The Church was right both biblically and scientifically. There is no conflict between Scripture and true science. Whatever the Bible says is so, even on matters of science.

Copernicus, Kepler, and Galileo were all smart scientists, but they were all wrong. The canonized view of geocentrism was based on Scripture and true science, not the ancient intellectuals Ptolemy and Aristotle.

Heliocentrism is a pseudoscientific explanation. Geocentrism is both a biblical and scientific explanation. The Bible is a geocentric book.

Tycho Brahe

Tycho Brahe (1546-1601), the renowned Danish astronomer, was born three years after Copernicus died. He rejected the Copernican System that had begun to be accepted. Brahe explained the movements of the heavenly bodies geocentrically, much as they had been explained throughout history. He placed the Earth at the center of the heavens and all the bodies orbiting around it.

Tycho Brahe's model has not been disproved. Brahe's non-moving Earth model is used today in all the applied sciences including practical astronomy, space travel, and eclipse predictions.

The entire world has been indoctrinated to believe that the heliocentric Copernican Model is true, but Brahe's geocentric (non-moving) Earth model still provides the basis for calculations which demand precision and accuracy. All airline pilots calculate the takeoff and landing of their airplane based upon a non-moving Earth. Also, space engineers calculate the liftoff and landing of space capsules based upon a non-moving Earth.

History - Galileo Defended Heliocentrism

In 1632, Galileo published Dialogue Concerning the Two Chief World System, in which he defended the heliocentric model. In response to rising controversy over his theology, his astronomy (that the Earth and planets orbit the Sun) and his philosophy, the Roman Inquisition tried Galileo in 1633 and found him "vehemently suspect of heresy," sentencing him to indefinite imprisonment. Galileo was held under house arrest until his death in 1642.

The best common sense and design arguments against the heliocentricity myth have to do with the motions and speeds required of the Earth in that model.

Reflect on the basics of the requirements for the heliocentric myth and begin to grasp the ludicrousness of it all....

The heliocentric myth has to ratchet up the Earth's speed to approximately 67,000 mph to get it around the sun in its alleged annual orbit. How fast? Over thirty times rifle bullet speed! The clouds, birds, and jet flights take no notice.

The stationary Earth taught in the Bible is confirmed by everything that is actually observed...by every experiment performed...by all eclipse and navigation and satellite realities. A Rabbi-fostered religious movement is fraudulently using the Theoretical Science Establishment to destroy New Testament Christianity by destroying Bible Creation Credibility.

Copernicus developed the Heliocentric theory. However, he did not release his new theory until near death because he knew that it contradicted the Bible.

It was not until the early 17th century that Galileo and Johannes Kepler developed and popularized the Copernican theory, which for Galileo resulted in a trial and conviction for heresy. When Galileo began to promote the non-biblical and non-scientific theory of Heliocentrism, it caused a great controversy, which came to a head in the trial of Galileo by the Inquisition of 1632. The church was right; Galileo was wrong.

In the geocentric system, the Earth is considered to be the center of the solar system. The Moon, the planets, the Sun, and the stars all rotate around the Earth (which stays still), with uniform circular motion. They compose the heavens, which are considered to be ethereal and unchanging. The Earth is not rotating...nor is it going around the sun. Today's cosmology fulfills an anti-Bible religious plan disguised as "science." The whole scheme from Copernicanism to Big Bangism is a factless and unproven theory. These lies have planted the Truth-killing virus of evolutionism in every aspect of man's "knowledge" about the Cosmos, the Earth, and Yahweh Himself.

The evolution-based revolution sparked by Darwin, Marx and Freud in the late 1800s were dependent on the previous success of the Copernican revolution. The glue of false science: All False Science and all False Religion are held together by the weak, Bible-denying, indefensible Copernican Theory of a Rotating, Orbiting Earth. Both the theory of Darwinian evolutionism and the Copernican heliocentricity concept are phony, fake, and false.

Academic freedom is not allowed in the American educational system today. Geocentrism and scientific or biblical Creationism are not allowed to be taught in public schools, colleges and universities. Only one view is taught - Heliocentrism and Darwinian evolutionism.

It was the Copernican heliocentricity concept that gradually broke the back of Bible credibility as the source of Absolute Truth in Christendom. Once the Copernican Revolution had conquered the physical sciences of Astronomy and Physics and put down deep roots in Universities and lower schools everywhere, it was only a matter of time until the Biological sciences launched the Darwinian Revolution.

The Copernican Revolution not only declared the Bible wrong, it made the Earth and Mankind insignificant accidents in a universe full of stars/suns with fantasized planets and evolving life forms. It also provided an open door for theoretical science to steadily expand the age and size of the cosmos to fit the present Big Bang Kabbala Model of the Pharisee Religion.

The Geocentric model of the size and structure, age and purpose of the cosmos, the Earth, and mankind is 100% biblical, 100% scientifically viable, and 100% logical. This alternative model rests on the premise of a stationary Earth that is supported by all observational and experimental evidence. This solid premise reduces the size of the cosmos to less than one ten trillionth of what is cited in modern evolutionary textbooks today.

The truth about origins will expose every important religious and secular deception. The lie about a rotating and orbiting Earth is the necessary foundation for the success of a belief in a "creation scenario" that persuades the world that an evolutionary explanation for the origin of the cosmos, the Earth, and mankind is not "a scientific fact."

The embrace of Darwinian evolutionism quite predictably emboldened secular-minded people to further reject biblical absolutism and replace its teachings with yet more so-called new "truths" in areas of learning having to do with economics and government. Marxism had been unsuccessful and floundering, but was given new life as a result.

Over the centuries the Copernican deception has made a cataclysmic impact on every field of modern man's knowledge and education.

The evolution-based revolutions sparked by the Darwin/Marx/Freud triumvirate in the late 1800s was totally dependent on the previous success of the Copernican Revolution.

Science - Michelson and Morley Experiment

The Michelson and Morley experiments "dumbfounded" heliocentric scientists the world over because it consistently showed a non-moving Earth.

Physicist A.A. Michelson (1852-1931) and Chemist E.W. Morley (1838-1923) devised a unique instrument for measuring and comparing the speed of light at various angles as the instrument, along with the Earth, rushed through space. The science establishment was locked into the Copernican-Newton model for at least 200 years, as were Michelson and Morley. They were not challenging the Copernican-Newton model; they assumed it to be true. They were not trying to prove that the Earth moved. They were trying to prove a point about the way light behaves when its source is in motion.

Michelson had designed and tested an "interferometer" in Berlin in 1881-1882. It gave the very unexpected and unacceptable result that the earth was not moving. In 1883, he continued to refine his "interferometer" which, continued to show no Earth movement. In 1887, along with Morley, they officially described the experiment and released the results. These two scientists totally supported the Copernican view. The "interferometer" did not do what it was supposed to do and what it actually did do was contrary to the Copernican view. The experiment showed the light returned simultaneously from both directions which meant the earth was not moving. That meant a motionless earth was not orbiting the sun at over 67,000 mph. The light rays could not be allowed to return simultaneously because the Earth was not moving. This experiment was performed over a period of years before and after 1887 by different scientists in different countries. The light rays always returned simultaneously on both arms of the interferometer and the fringes always remained on the same side year-round.

The entire reputation of the secular science establishment was at stake. It had to be moving. Any explanation no matter how crazy and unscientific it was just had to be found.

Scientists all over the world were in a nervous panic. Their fake theory was falling apart. This result was totally unacceptable. It put the scientific world in perplexity. They had to find a way out of their dilemma. This was serious trouble. The whole heliocentric cult with its "science" idol was in jeopardy. For over three centuries of carefully laid propaganda and indoctrination the Copernican Revolution had discounted and overcome the biblical account of a stationary Earth.

In 1859, Charles Darwin's Origin of Species broke through the second line of defense with the Evolution battering ram. This was designed to defeat and bury the Creation account of man created in the image of God and the Genesis record of Creation. Evolutionists deny and discredit six-day Creation, the Garden of Eden, the existence of Satan, temptation, the Fall of man, the need of salvation for Jesus to redeem man in his fallen condition. Evolutionists teach that man evolved from apelike creatures over millions of years. They also deny the rock and fossil records - layers of dead things buried in rock layers all over the world as a result of the Noahic Flood.

Spirit led Christians must unite and rally behind the Bible's 67 geocentric verses and drive the idol worshipers back across the wall, and the Evolutionists along with them. We need Christian leaders to rise up and speak up, not sheeple who compromise with Evolutionism and Heliocentrism.

The bottom line is that the negative results of the Michelson-Morley interferometer experiments conducted in Europe and the U.S. in the 1880s consistently showed no orbital motion of the Earth around the sun. No motion. Period. Shades of Joshua: "Sun, stand still!" (Joshua10:12). The sun was moving and God stopped it and the moon too, in broad daylight.

But the halfwits in the "science" cult weren't stopped by the Michelson results.

How did these deceptive liars get out of their worst nightmare?
Einstein.

Einstein vs Euclid

The Word of God is absolute truth. LAWS of science are unchangeable truths. Nobody can disregard these LAWS and come up with something that conflicts with and denies true LAWS and call that new idea a new truth when it is a lie. Geometry is the exact science of measuring the distance between various points. The sum of the interior angles of a triangle is 180 degrees. No more, no less.

Euclid (c. 300 BC) of Alexandria (Egypt) was a Greek mathematician, the most prominent mathematician of Greco-Roman antiquity. He was often referred to as the "father of geometry," and is best known for his treatise on geometry, the Elements. For thousands of years the final authority on this subject was Euclid. He spelled out everything on the subject and it all worked.

Along came Albert Einstein, who invented a new anti-Euclidian geometry. It would do what the scientific establishment wanted it to do. He got the unscientific idea from Riemann and Minkowski. Accordingly, he threw out 2 + 2 = 4 geometry, and now triangles no longer equaled 180 degrees. Nevertheless, the three angles of a triangle are not more than 180 degrees. Changing geometry smacks of calling black white, and white black. Riemann-Minkowski is the foundation of the relativity of Einstein. Einstein's General Relativity theory (1905) is simply not true. Einstein used his own symbols, his own word meanings, and spherical trigonometry, his own invented math. A person can "prove" anything that way. Einstein and Relativity and Darwin and Evolutionism are lies from A to Z. There is nothing scientific about evolutionism or heliocentrism. Einstein and all the 2 + 2 = 5 mathematics have created a counterfeit of God's real cosmos. But the truth never changes. 2 + 2 = 4. All of Einstein's mathematics began with the "fact" that 2 + 2 = 5. Einstein's Relativity is totally dependent upon Non-Euclidian geometry. A totally honest scientist refuses to have any part of the 2 + 2 = 5 kind of math and insists on sticking to the 2 + 2 = 4 kind of math.

Einstein "borrowed" the ideas from others. They made no sense and those who claimed to understand them when they did not made no difference. They were certainly confusing, abstruse, and smothered in mathematical decorations and scientific mushrooms and onions to serve the purpose of distracting and discounting what the Bible clearly says about a non-moving Earth.

The one conclusion demanded by The Theory of Relativity is that there is no Absolute Truth. All things are relative. Applied to the matter of whether the Earth is moving or not, the Theory simply says that all motion is relative to where you are when you observe something moving and that there is nothing standing still in the whole cosmos. Einstein began with the assumption that the Earth is moving. He paid no attention to that specific matter at all.

It was "unthinkable" that the secular science establishment could go back to Brahe's geocentrism, so Einstein, along with the rest of the pseudoscience establishment, refused to address the subject directly and openly. Together, they started with the false premise that the Earth is moving.

Einstein sidestepped a head-on confrontation with the issue. Everything he did was done behind a mathematical smoke-screen which was designed to cover up the fact that he was indeed dealing with the central issue and dealing with it in a way that was intended to put a stop to anyone claiming that the Earth stands still.

Einstein's Relativity concept does not in any way prove that the earth is moving. He claimed there is nothing at rest in the cosmos, so it is pointless to talk about a stationary Earth. The bottom line was that there is no such thing as Truth when it comes to Euclid's geometry and the Bible's geocentrism. His idea of no true or false has since escalated into no black and white, no right and wrong, no good or bad behavior as well as scientific, artistic, economic or whatever. The idea that everything is relative has been pounded into people's heads for almost a century. That does not make it true. It cannot be true because it contradicts the Word of God.

Heliocentric "science" demands that the moon is going eastward. Bible science demands that the moon is going westward. Both the sun and the moon are going east to west over a non-moving Earth every day. It's what the Bible says and what the data from empirical evidence shows. This is an Absolute Truth.

All the fancy footwork involving invented mathematics, new definitions for time and distance, arbitrary absolutes, thought experiments instead of real experiments was just an "intellectual" smoke-screen designed to keep anybody from noticing the true and only purpose which was to bury the non-moving Earth taught in the Bible. Einstein was the chief engineer of this 1905 masterpiece of deception. He was anti-Bible, false science's hero and savior. He received adulation from the world-wide anti-bible establishment during his lifetime. It was fitting for the one who rescued the pseudoscientific establishment from the disgrace of utter embarrassment and defeat that it would suffer if it had to admit that heliocentrism and all that had labored so hard to build upon it were wrong and the Bible was right.

Anyone who gives any credence to Einstein and his pseudoscientific theories has been deceived and does not realize that he was just a paid hack for the heliocentric model.

Deception

There is a deception-controlled network of the media/MSM, etc., that advances anti-biblical teaching of origins. In some cases, even in supposedly Bible-believing churches, colleges, and publishing houses, a biblical Christian worldview gets suppressed in terms of origins.

The same kind of censorship is in almost total control of all areas of knowledge and learning in high schools, colleges and universities: Natural Sciences, Social Sciences, and Arts and Humanities.

Counterfeit

Counterfeit $20 bills have flaws. Heliocentrism is as phony as a counterfeit $20 bill. That which is imperfect has flaws in it. The flaws are always there. Only a trained expert can discover its flaws.

LOGIC

Logically, all counterfeits have discoverable flaws.

Logically, also, when there are only two things to compare and one must be true (as with heliocentricity and geocentricity), then the discovery of flaws in one proves not only that it is the counterfeit, it also proves at the same time that the other one is both flawless and the real thing, the genuine article, the Truth.

A self-styled genius has a problem with logic.

Today, just about everything called "education" for the last several generations has been based upon or derived from man's counterfeit of biblical Truth involved in Creation. Student's should be taught to question everything because teachers don't know everything.

There always are observable flaws in anything that is a counterfeit. There are observable flaws in the Copernican System which is taught world-wide today as scientific fact. The bottom line on Copernicanism: nothing but flaws. The same goes for Evolutionism. There is not one thing true about it! Every claim that it makes rests on an assumption that violates an observable fact. No one has ever observed the Earth moving. No one. No test or space capsule shot has ever shown the Earth to move. None of them.

The use of this concept to claim proof for the Earth's rotation is a hoax of a high order.

This does not prove the Earth is moving!

Foucault's Pendulum

Foucault's Pendulum was conceived and produced for one purpose alone, namely, to "prove" the Earth's rotation. This Pendulum, in reality, is a pseudoscientific fraud, a cunningly devised deception designed to persuade the world that "Science" has proof that the Earth revolves on an axis (and hence orbits the sun). But Foucault's "Pendulum" doesn't prove that at all.

Viewers who see this contraption assume that this Pendulum is giving observable proof that the Earth is moving. They are falsely told on the signs that they are viewing a scientific demonstration which proves the Earth is moving. Young people have been indoctrinated during their school years to believe that the Earth is rotating on an axis and orbiting the sun. This "educational" display places doubt on the Bible and tells them that life on Earth has been evolving for three billion years and that they are the result of this evolutionary process. And that Adam and Eve are mythical characters.

Foucault's Pendulum is a counterfeit of a true pendulum. IT IS NOT A TRUE PENDULUM. It is, rather, nothing more than a diabolically clever contrivance leaning on the sound reputation of true pendulums for its credibility and purporting to show a rotating Earth (and the Bible in error).

If the Foucault Pendulum is not disturbed by the earth's rotation, how, then, is it that the atmosphere must follow that motion? Can an eagle soaring up in New York State come down in California after two hours having, together with the surrounding air, been undisturbed by the rapidly moving earth? The evolutionist's dream of great pressure to support this theory. The great pressure cannot be proven. We cannot put a limit to the atmosphere above us. We must accept it as a fact that the whole space around us is filled with air. It is a well-known property of the air to fill all empty space. The air possesses a tendency toward expansion. As to hydrogen, the Copernicans must admit, against their theory, that the earth cannot hold its hydrogen. It is produced abundantly on the earth, but does not remain here. Where does it stay? It escapes into space. And this seems very natural, since, according to modern science, a material medium called ether, a fine elastic substance, fills all space. Why not, then, call it by one name and say, our atmosphere extends into all surrounding space connecting the earth with sun, moon, and stars, and being the carrier of light and electricity. True, this does not agree with the embraced theory, but it agrees very well with science and the Bible.

The Smithsonian

The Smithsonian in Washington, DC is one of the most high-class propaganda organs for Darwinian evolution. Modern space technology is equipped with so-called geosynchronous satellites and sends photographic images promoting Copernicanism. The "U.S. Space and Rocket Center" in Huntsville, Alabama promotes evolutionism and the coming New World Order clothed in Environmental Protection Agency garments.

Space is not the last frontier for man; Heaven is! The Truth about the origin and the immovable nature of this beautiful blue Earth at the center of the cosmos is all described in the Scriptures. Proof of a motionless Earth is inescapable and undeniable.

Satan's triplet deceptions that must be defeated are: (1) Darwinian evolutionism; (2) The Copernican Revolution lie known as heliocentrism; and (3) The Spherical spinning Earth.

LOGIC
One of the following statements must be true and one must be false:
1. The Earth is moving. (Heliocentrism)
2. The Earth is not moving. (Geocentricism)

Saying something is true and believing something is true can't make it true if it is false. That would not be logical.

Ether - Rarified Element

Ether: the upper regions of space or the rarified element supposed to fill those regions. Ether is defined as a "rarified element" that is supposed to exist in all the spaces between stars, planets, comets, and so on.

That's what it was until Einstein declared on his blackboard that it did not exist. There are logical contradictions galore. Einstein said there was no ether, but this was a direct contradiction to Maxwell's basic axiom, that ether existed.

In 1865, James Clerk Maxwell published his seminal treatise, The Dynamical Theory of the Electromagnetic Field. In his treatise, Maxwell posited that there must be a substance through which electromagnetic phenomena occur. He called this substance "ether."

Einstein found a way of saving Maxwell's equations. He said only the equations needed to be saved. The physical part of the Theory was expendable. Einstein foisted his logical sleight-of-hand on the world.

This is rubbery mathematics. Why did Einstein need so desperately to get rid of ether? Ether served as an absolute standard. Einstein's Special Relativity Theory says there are no absolutes. Einstein could have nothing at rest in the universe. In Einstein's universe everything has to be moving. Nothing could be stationary, motionless, even the ether.

Man could no longer consider, believe, or even conceive of an Earth that was "at rest, hung on nothing, that it can not be moved" as the Bible says it is.

Einstein and all the Relativists who have controlled physics and astronomy throughout the past century said "ether" was nothing. The dictionary definition says "ether" is something.

Science at the Crossroads

Herbert Dingle (1890-1978) was an English astronomer and President of the Royal Astronomical Society. He became convinced that Einstein's theory of relativity cannot be true since it contains certain logical impossibilities. When he tried to publish critical investigations, he soon found that such work was not accepted. Dingle believed that something ought to be said, so, in 1972, he had recourse to publishing his book entitled, Science at the Crossroads.

Dingle came to doubt the foundations of Einstein's work on the theory of relativity after reading an account of the so-called twin paradox - the rates of the clocks: a clock at the distant point had been artificially set to agree with the freely adopted definition, and the fact that the traveler's clock disagreed with it did not mean that it would disagree with the Earth clock, which had not been artificially set to agree with any definition.

It appears that Dingle's challenge, although coming from an eminent authority and author of textbooks on relativity, was not given space. Thus, he explained his criticisms by publishing Science at the Crossroads, which challenged Einstein's lack of commonsense in the matter.

The Michelson-Morley experiment had shown that if there was ether then the Earth was not moving. Einstein, willy-nilly, declared the ether null and void, and declared without saying a word, that the Earth was moving because there wasn't anything in the cosmos that wasn't moving. This is not a scientific fact.

How fast does the Earth move? Spinning on its axis, earth moves at 1,038 MPH at the equator, 67,000 MPH around the sun annually, and 500,000 yet another way without flying to pieces. This meant that space could not have anything in it, no ether at all; for if it did, there would have to be some friction at those speeds and any friction whatsoever would blow away the Earth's atmosphere and the topsoil.

Battle of the Bulge

The idea of a "bulge" as the result of a supposed rotation of the Earth slinging tons of dirt to the middle of the Earth at the equator is a load of dusty lies. Why doesn't it sling off the spinning earth into space? Astronomer Fred Hoyle told a big lie when he said, "It is well known that as a consequence of its rotation the equatorial diameter of the earth exceeds the polar diameter by about 27 miles - the Earth is slightly squashed at its poles."

All the evolutionary science textbooks support this lie. This idea takes a lot of bizarre theorizing about how the "bulge" (over 142,000 feet out of round) adjusts itself to keep the Earth from toppling over. It's mind-blowing the extremes of theorizing that are required to keep up the lie of a moving Earth! There are no photographs taken from outer space of the Earth to give any hard, factual evidence of a bulge.

There is no bulge because there is no rotation, which means no orbiting, which means Copernicanism is proven wrong.

Conclusions:
- Copernicanism is deception!
- Einstein is a deceiver.
- Relativity is another deception!

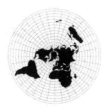

"THE LAW OF UNIVERSAL GRAVITATION"

As part of the world-wide indoctrination into heliocentrism, there had to be a mechanism to explain the motions of the heavenly bodies, what keeps them in their places. That mechanism is called "The Law of Universal Gravitation." It is credited to Newton but was first formulated by Kepler. It is an absolutely baseless concept which violates and contradicts its essential magnetic principal every second of every day, year in and year out.

Tides

Gravity does not explain the tides. Universal gravitation is a bankrupt hypothesis just the same as Darwin's "natural selection" mechanism is now being recognized as a bankrupt and hopeless hypothesis that is incapable of explaining evolutionism.

Eclipses

There are two kinds of eclipses: Solar (Sun) and Lunar (Moon).

When the Moon blocks out the Sun, it's a solar eclipse. When the Earth blocks out the Moon, it's a lunar eclipse.

Eclipse means: "The obstruction of light from one celestial body by another."

The Encyclopedia Britannica has a sub-heading: "Prediction and Calculation of Solar and Lunar Eclipses." It reveals two things: first, it tells when an eclipse will occur, and second, when and where it will be visible. FIRST, WE MUST CONSIDER THE EARTH AS FIXED. These precise and accurate statistics about where the shadow goes during an eclipse are arrived at on the basis of a non-moving, totally stationary, i.e., "fixed" Earth.

The shadow could not go the same way if the Earth is rotating a thousand mph as it would if it is standing still! It's not a matter of convenience to use a fixed Earth to get the right results. The same results cannot be achieved based on a rotating Earth.

Fact One: The shadow from a solar eclipse goes a certain direction. Fact Two: That direction is precisely predictable before the eclipse occurs. Fact Three: Those precise predictions are achieved by starting with a "fixed" (non-moving) Earth. Fact Four: The calculations that are achieved and are based on a fixed Earth could not and should not come out right if they were applied to an Earth that is rotating 1,038 mph at the equator.

Ecliptic calculations are based upon and can only apply to a non-moving Earth. This does not work exactly and precisely the same on an Earth that is moving faster than the speed of sound in one direction, 30 times as fast as a rifle bullet in another direction, and 250 times as fast as a rifle bullet in yet another direction. No way!

The direction which the shadow goes during all solar eclipses is always eastward. This phenomenon provides us with a graphic demonstration of the absence of the Coriolis effect! We realize the necessity of basing predictions about the shadow's course on a "fixed" Earth!

Calculations based on a fixed Earth work for one reason: The Earth IS fixed! There is no wiggle room.

Paradoxes

1 + 1 = 3

When "scientists" run into a contradiction they call it a "paradox." It's still a contradiction, regardless of what it's called. It's like putting perfume on a pig. It's still a pig.

There is a contradiction (paradox) when anybody starts out by saying something is true which is not true. A single paradox can obliterate an entire theoretical structure.

The entire support of Copernicanism is expressed in mathematical terms. Mathematics is the whole bag as far as "evidence" for a moving Earth is concerned. There is no real evidence, so the whole idea is worked out with some kind of phony mathematics invented for the purpose they want. Letters and symbols equal whatever mathematicians agree they equal.

A "paradox" is just a fancy word for a contradiction that contains a lie. The sciences of physics and astronomy are riddled with paradoxes.

Gaseous Envelope

The Copernicans get away with answering most of their observable problems by saying that the whole atmosphere around the Earth is an attached "envelope" that rotates with the Earth. This is Nonsense.

The movement of clouds, birds, bees, butterflies, airplanes, etc., is explained by this so-called "envelope." The Earth's atmosphere and gaseous envelope is marked return to sender, address unknown; no such number, no such zone. This is not reality. Supposedly, these ECLIPSE SHADOWS ORIGINATE BEYOND that atmospheric "envelope!" Those shadows are then projected like a laser beam through the "envelope" for three hours or more during an eclipse.

The Bottom Line:

The shadow (laser beam) always goes where it is predicted it will go because the calculations behind those predictions are based on a non-moving, fixed, static, immobile, stationary, unchanging, inert, motionless Earth.

The "envelope" is like a protective bubble for the clouds, birds, bees, butterflies, airplanes, etc., to stay velcroed in Earth's non-moving atmosphere. You can't have it both ways.

Calculations that have always produced these accurate predictions have always been based on a non-moving Earth.

Copernicus, Kepler, Galileo, Einstein, Sagan all rely on funny mathematics to reach their faulty conclusions. A "laser beam" should be put through their bogus blackboards and destroy their imaginary calculations. Nobody makes eclipse predictions based on a moving Earth. It can't be done!

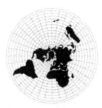

HYPERSPACES

What is the nature of reality? A hyperspace is a term used for the study of spaces of more than three dimensions. Time is not a fourth dimension.

Spherical (3-D) Trigonometry

If a triangle adds up to more than 180°, you have not encountered the curvature of the earth because the earth is a flat plane, not a round ball. You cannot have a triangle with 90° in each corner.

Euclid was right. There are only 180° in a triangle. No more, until Einstein, but he was wrong. Einstein had a heliocentric agenda. If you go beyond Euclid, you've gone too far. Non-euclidean geometry is Einstein's fantasy to prove the earth is moving. He was a failed scientist with bushy hair.

Beyond Euclid (3+ Dimensions)

These are mere models. They are not scientifically defensible. They are not reality.

Whenever you go beyond Euclid, you've gone too far.

There are not more than three dimensions we live in. This is all conjecture. That's jecture with a con.

Superstrings are conjecture.

10-dimensions are conjecture.

Conjecture means: speculation, hypothesis, possibility, theory, guess, supposition, surmise. You know, what if?

Einstein and others made up the additional dimensions and wanted to integrate them into a common model. They wanted to integrate electromagnetic power and nuclear forces. Look out!

NASA CGI Globe

The Terrestrial Globe

The earliest existing terrestrial globe was created in 1492 by Martin Behaim (1459-1537) with the help of a painter named Georg Glockendon. Behaim was a German mapmaker, navigator, and merchant. Working in Nuremberg, Germany, he took flat maps, cut them into sections, and then pasted them on a round ball. He called his globe the "Nuremberg Terrestrial Globe." The map of the globe was stretched into a circular shape. It was not terrestrial, it was earthly.

Did you know that on the underside of the base of a model globe sold in stores is a sticker that reads:

Not For Educational Purposes, But For Decorative Purposes.

Globalists know the Continents on the model globe are out of proportion with the actual shape and size of the Earth. You can't fit the flat earth map on a round ball globe.

Gleason's New Standard Map Of The World

Gleason's 1894 New Standard Map Of The World is a Flat Earth Map.

SCIENTIFIC - Produced by Cartographer and Civil Engineer Alexander Gleason (circa 1892)

AUTHENTIC - Originally Published by the Buffalo Type and Engraving Company, Buffalo, NY

ACCURATE - Flat Earth Map of the World As "It Is" - Scientifically and Practically Correct!

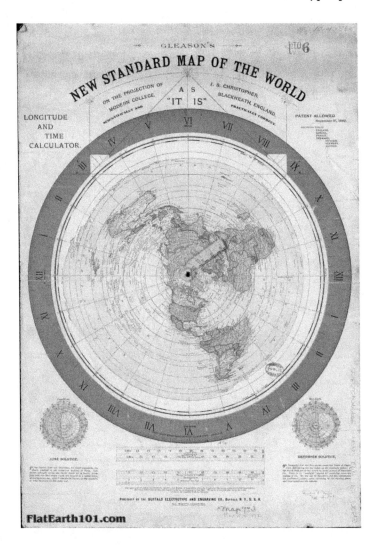

PLAYING WITH THE DEVIL

He who plays with the devil loses. When Satan spoke to Eve in the garden, he was nice to her. Nothing about his appearance or his tone of voice made her fearful. Eve did not know she was being deceived. Satan deceived her with smooth words filled with half truths and lies. She played with the devil and lost.

Government schools, state colleges and universities are nice to their students, but they are teaching them half-truths and lies. The students don't know they are being deceived and indoctrinated. Day after day they hear Darwinian evolutionist lies, heliocentric lies, and spherical spinning earth lies. That's all they know.

Regrettably, many fundamentalist pastors and professors in Christian schools and universities have been indoctrinated with the same half-truths and lies in the schools they attended. Thus, they are not comfortable with the many passages in the Bible that clearly support the geocentric model and the flat-earth model. Flat-earth should not be considered a theory due to all the biblical texts and true scientific evidence that support it. Evolution is a theory that has never been proven because there is no real evidence to support it. The arguments for a non-moving earth and a flat-earth come from both the Bible and reliable scientific evidence. Paul warned Timothy about the opposing ideas of what is falsely called knowledge (1 Timothy 6:20-21). The Darwinian evolutionary hypothesis, the heliocentric model, and global ball model are all pseudoscience. False science masquerading as observable phenomena. They are based on unproven assumptions. Of course, you cannot exclude divine revelation about Creation. The supposition that the earth is a round spinning ball is based upon pseudoscience. Fundamentalist and evangelical pastors and college professors have compromised, capitulated, accommodated, rationalized and reinterpreted the particular passages to defend their narrow-minded faith that their KJV Bible is without error. They chose to believe the secular science community over the inerrant written Word of God. They went along to get along. They chose popularity over increasing righteousness. Secular science is the enemy of what the Bible says, and whatever the Bible says is so. They cannot get away with this kind of Scripture twisting. Their capitulation with the secular science community has resulted in a messy history.

Many unsuspecting young people who have attended government public schools in America have been outright lied to about heliocentrism, about the Earth being a globe, Darwinian evolution, millions of years, the age of the earth, the fossil record, the Big Bang theory, general relativity, homosexuality, same-gender marriage, critical race theory (CRT), skin color and racism, global warming, socialism, Marxism, Communism, big government, and judicial activism. These naive young people believed all these lies because that's all they have ever been taught since childhood over and over again, and no one challenged them. This is indoctrination, not education.

If you attended a college or university, Christian or non-Christian, and were taught in an astronomy class the heliocentric model, that the earth goes around the sun every 24 hours, you wasted your time and money. If you attended a college or university, Christian or non-Christian, and were taught in a cosmology class that the earth is a ball globe, spins at 1,038 mph, and is tilted on an axis at 23.4 degrees, you wasted your time and money. Anyone who teaches these models as fact is a false teacher.

You are a victim of educational malpractice. There were three key things taught in every public school classroom in America when George Washington went to school. All three have been banned by the federal government from today's schools, and from the schools you went to.

You probably spent 17 years of your life in government-approved classrooms, and they were sanitized from the three most important things that would give you a balanced biblical worldview. They are:

- Genesis record of creation—In the beginning God created
- Geocentric Model—non-moving earth
- Flat Earth model—earth is a flat plane

A comprehensive online home study program can duplicate a colonial American public school education in the essential points you were deprived of.

America was the most prosperous and admired nation in human history. When America turned her back on early educational precepts and philosophy the United States became morally and ethically bankrupt. When did this happen?

Piece by piece, the Federal Government prohibited public schools from following the educational philosophy of the Old Deluder Satan Act of 1647. This Massachusetts law laid the basis for public schools in America. Every community should teach children how to read so they can read and understand the Bible and not be deceived by Satan. The colonial public school curriculum that made America the most prosperous and admired nation in history transformed young people into becoming:

- an extraordinary American
- an extraordinary Christian
- an extraordinary Human Being

CGI

We live in a CGI world. What does CGI stand for? Computer-generated imagery (CGI), which is the use of computer graphics in art and media. It is the use of computer graphics to create or contribute to images. "CGI" is applied in the 3-D graphics used in TV weather forecasts and radar storm alerts.

Does NASA lie to us? We can be fooled by 2-D images. Do we live on a circular earth? The images we see are CGI that are photo shopped images. NASA uses a fisheye lens. A fisheye lens is an ultra wide-angle lens that produces visual distortion intended to create a wide panoramic or hemispherical image. The pictures of the earth taken from space are layer upon layer CGI photo shopped images.

United Nations Emblem and Flag

The UN emblem is a map of the flat earth. In 1946, the UN knew the earth was a flat plane. The UN emblem was designed to be "a map of the world representing an azimuthal equidistant projection centered on the North Pole, inscribed in a wreath consisting of crossed conventionalized branches of the olive tree, in gold on a field of smoke-blue with all water areas in white. The projection of the map extends to 60 degrees south latitude, and includes five concentric circles."

UNITED NATIONS

The flag of the United Nations was adopted on December 7, 1946, and consists of the official emblem of the United Nations in white on a blue background. The olive branches are a symbol for peace. The blue color that appears in the background of the insignia was chosen to be "the opposite of red, the war color."

Propaganda From the Secular Science Community

We live on a spherical planet called Earth spinning at 1,000 mph on a 23.4° tilt. That's 23.4° away from vertical. That leaves 66.6o away from horizontal.

We are orbiting an ordinary star (Sun) that is 93 million miles away from the Earth.

The Sun is embedded in a galaxy of 100 billion stars that is one of trillions of galaxies in an infinite and expanding void.

Human beings are insignificant and unimportant microbes who arrived on the Earth by accident and are crawling around on a speck of dust.

CGI Photographic Unreality

NASA's so-called photographic evidence of the Earth taken from space is called the Big Blue Marble. It's CGI. Photo-shopped. Video is not reality.

CGI are composites; layer upon layer

Color of oceans are vivid through miles of atmosphere

Clouds look strange or static

Use of different maps: The Gall-Peters Projection Map vs Mercator Projection Map. Changes in the size of continents.

Use of a fisheye lens to make the flat plane Earth look curved. It's what all TV weather reporting use.

Flying in an airplane, the horizon always arises to your eye level. Horizon sight line. On a globe, the expected horizon would be below you.

The Sun is 3,100 miles away and 34 miles across. The sun has an isolated hotspot on Earth as it orbits from east to west. The sun warms the atmosphere as it rises in the east. The sun is the hottest at high noon. It's warmer at the equator because the sun crosses it twice on its circuit above the earth. The sun orbits the earth in an elliptical (oval-shaped) pattern every 24 hours. The sun remains 3,100 miles above the earth's surface at all times. The Sun's radiation does not heat space as a vacuum is a perfect insulator, like a thermos. Without an atmosphere to conduct or convect the heat away the temperature will rise to over 2,000 degrees Celsius or 4,532 degrees Fahrenheit. Objects in space would glow and melt.

There is a long canal in Cambridgeshire, England that runs straight for a length of six miles. The water is level from end to end. Starting in 1838, Samuel Rowbotham conducted the Bedford Level experiment. It was series of observations carried out along a six-mile length of the Old Bedford River. He placed a telescope at one end of a canal. The telescope was six inches above the surface of the water and he was able to observe a boat with a flag on it the entire journey until at the other end of the canal. He claimed that he had proven the earth to be flat. If the earth was curved, the boat would have been 16 feet lower at the other end of the canal. The earth does not have a curvature.

The human body has senses that detect changes in velocity. If the earth is spinning, why don't we feel dizzy? Why don't we lose our hat? Secular scientists say the Earth is spinning the fastest at the equator - over 1,000 mph.

The motion of the stars do not prove that the earth is spinning. The earth is static and unchanging. It is fixed. It appears that the stars are rotating in a circle around Polaris east to west. If the Earth were wobbling as it is spinning at 1,000 mph, any small change in Earth's position would mean that the polar axis would no longer point to Polaris many miles away. If you were to set up a camera on a tripod in the night sky and point it toward the North Star, Polaris, which does not move, and leave it on for a long exposure you would get a pattern of star trails around Polaris. You wouldn't see the perfect circular pattern of stars in the night sky if the Earth was spinning. Secular scientists hate circles. Where's the motion?

If you look down a very long corridor, the walls, the ceiling, and the floor all converge. It's a matter of perspective.

Every month the Moon goes through eight (8) phases, always the same eight, always in the same order. The Moon is uniform over the entire surface. If it was a sphere reflecting the sun then the curved surface would display a highlight and drop-off. Moonlight is cold with a putrid odor. The sun is hot with a sweet odor. Eco balance. The Moon is self luminous and not reflecting the sun. Mark 13:24 tells us, "the moon will not give its light." This means the moon gives its own light. Revelation 21:23 says the city in heaven has no need of sun or moon to shine on it. Both the sun and moon are shining. 1 Corinthians 15:41says the sun and the moon and the stars each have their own glory. The moon has another kind of splendor. Ezekiel 32:7 says the sun and the moon are the same size, and the moon will not give its light. Jeremiah 31:35 says the LORD gives the sun for light by day and the ordinances (decrees) of the moon and stars to shine by night. Isaiah 13:10 says the moon will not shed its light. Everybody sees the same Moon no matter where they are on Earth. The Moon is closer to Earth than evolutionists claim. The Moon is not 238,855 miles away from the Earth. The average distance between the Earth and the Moon is 3,000 miles. The Sun and the Moon are the same size (34 miles across) and the same distance from the Earth. That's why they look the same size during an eclipse.

There are no telecommunication satellites in space. Just photo-shopped images. Satellites are a work of fiction. NASA and the US government work together to hide the truth from the American people. To transmit, they use a radio triangulation system. Telephone calls are handled by underground fiber optic cables. Shortwave radio can also span long distances.

Space shuttles go straight up when they launch, then it travels horizontally above the Earth. A space shuttle becomes a glider after it separates from the rocket booster. Actually, it's a jet with jet engines. It never does go into orbit.

Space walks are faked. Space walks are done in water tanks. It's an illusion.

Not one of the seven astronauts aboard the space shuttle Challenger disaster died in the explosion in 1986. It was all faked. Six of the seven are still alive today.

If the earth is spinning at 1,000 mph, then every airplane attempting to make a landing would miss the runway.

There is a lack of direct flights in the Southern Hemisphere, which is south of the equator. They switch off all GPS trackers in the Southern Hemisphere. They switch the GPS tracker back on one hour before landing.

The North Pole is in the center of the flat Earth with the land mass surrounding it. The South Pole does not exist. The ends of the Earth is the 200 feet high ice wall surrounding the entire flat Earth like a rim. It keeps all the water from the oceans in place. What would you see if visiting Antarctic? A 200 foot high wall of ice followed by 300 miles of Antarctic desert with no life, no vegetation, and temperatures dropping to -100 degrees Centigrade. Then you encounter a mountain range 2 miles high. The mountains are called the Rockefeller Mountains with a plateau at the top.

How does the secular science community get the world to believe this pseudoscience? Indoctrination. The model round globe tilted on an axis is a false idol and propaganda tool. It represents what is not as though it is real. It's seen in every business office, classroom and library in the world. Most homes have a globe model. It's used in movies and on TV shows. The language we use reflects a global sphere. Global finance. Global trade. Around the globe. Global outreach. Go global. Think global. All the actors in the fake story are members of the same club. Ptolemy was a Mason. Copernicus was a Jesuit priest. Sir Isaac Newton was a free mason. All the astronauts are free masons. They all tell the same story.

NASA Logo

NASA put a red snake tongue in their logo. It represents the devil, who is the father of lies (John 8:44). NASA speaks with forked tongue. NASA was formed with Nazi scientists transplanted to America after WWII. See: Operation Paperclip. The Nazi approach to propaganda is: "If you tell a big lie often enough and keep repeating it, people will eventually come to believe it..."

The goal of our enemy is to bring as many people as possible under their control. The enemy's purpose is to steal and kill and destroy. The modern day Big Bang theory is atheistic. The evolutionary paradigm and the heliocentric global earth model are based on time and chance. The godless secular science community attempts to control humanity by removing God and any sort of Intelligent design. Their objective is to replace a purposeful Divine creation with a haphazard random cosmic coincidence.

JERUSAELEM vs. ATHENS

The Geocentric Model is Jerusalem. The Heliocentric Model is Athens. The conflict between Jerusalem and Athens is a spiritual conflict. One is spiritual and the other is secular. The Geocentric Model is plain science. The Heliocentric Model is junk science.

Since 1635 in Boston, the American public education system has morphed into Athens. Every nation on earth is a theocracy at some level. Christian Theocracy is where Elohim of Creation is God. A "secular" theocracy is where every man is his own "god." Science is god in the Darwinian evolutionary community.

BIBLICAL WORLDVIEW OF TERRESTRIAL AND HEAVENLY BODIES

In 1 Corinthians 15:37-41, the Apostle Paul presents a science lesson by comparing the dissimilarity of different bodies. God gives a body to a bare seed of wheat or kernel of corn just as He planned. But what you sow is not the body that is to be. The bare seed dies and becomes a different form of life. To each of the seeds He gives a body of its own. These are the plant kind. All flesh is not the same. There are human kind, animal kind, bird kind and fish kind. God created each kind fully complete but with comparative dissimilarities. None of the kinds evolved into another kind. Human beings have one flesh, animals have another, birds and fish have another. Within the animal kind, bird kind and fish kind there are different species. Human kind do not have species or races. There is only one race—the human race with varying shades of brown skin.

Paul then presents a science lesson on heavenly bodies. The sun, the moon, and the stars are located in the second heaven. The glory of the heavenly body is of one sort. There is one glory of the sun, and another glory of the moon and another glory of the stars. There is only one sun and one moon but many stars. Each star has its own brightness that differs from the other stars as they orbit the Earth. The sun rules the day and the moon rules the night. Both the sun and the moon have their own glory. They are both lights. The moon is not a reflection of the sun, as both evolutionists and some indoctrinated creationists claim.

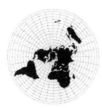

EARTH—A FLAT PLANE

Flat-earth is not a conspiracy theory. Rather, it is a model of a flat or level surface. A geometric plane is FLAT. Earth has some elevations and depressions, but overall, it is a flat plane. Why do some people think the Earth is flat? Because it is. There are three-flats. The sea is level. The Earth is a flat plane. Airbuses or jets fly level on an air plane. In between take-off and landing, a jet flies on a straight path or airline in the sky. The flat-Earth model is not an archaic conception of Earth's shape as a plane. Flat-Earth cosmography is both biblical and scientific. The branches of cosmography include astronomy, geography, and geology. The "Globe Theory" is just that, a theory. There are no scientific facts to support Earth's sphericity. Not one. Earth's sphericity is a pseudoscientific conspiracy theory. The Heliocentric world is a world of lies and deception. It is a misrepresentation of the cosmos. It's an imaginary world that Copernicus created ex nihilo. Modern flat-Earthers are happy, healthy, and in their right mind.

In 1865, Samuel Rowbotham published "Earth Not A Globe." It was an experimental inquiry into the true shape of the earth: proving it a flat plane without axial or orbital motion.

The true shape of the Earth, instead of it being a globe, and moving in space, it is the direct opposite - A PLANE; without motion, and unaccompanied by anything in the firmament similar to itself. Earth is a circular disc with a dome on top. It is an enclosed system.

If the earth is a globe with a circumference of 25,000 miles, the surface of all standing water must have a certain degree of convexity - every part must be an arc of a circle, curving from the peak at the rate of eight inches per mile multiplied by the square of the distance. Water seeks it own level. Water does not seek a perpendicular position. We say water in the oceans is at sea level. Water in the oceans is not curved or raised eight inches at one mile's distance; raised 32 inches at the distance of two miles; or raised 72 inches at the distance of three miles.

A pilot has never flown a jet aircraft around the world because the Earth is not a round ball globe. It is flat. However, a pilot has flown a jet aircraft over the earth or across the earth from continent to continent, but never around the earth. That is, up, up and over the top and then down, down, down as you go around. Nonsense. Flight time from La Guardia Airport (LGA) in New York City to the Amsterdam-Schiphol Airport (AMS) in Amsterdam, Netherlands is seven hours 17 minutes under normal conditions. The flight distance is 3,643 miles between cities. The time difference is six hours. Amsterdam time is six hours ahead of New York time. The flight pattern over the Atlantic Ocean is a straight line distance or direct flight distance between cities. The jet aircraft remains level while up in the air as the sea is level below. No nose dipping is required. The pilot sets the huge passenger aircraft on automatic pilot and drinks a cup of coffee. How high do passenger jets fly? The average commercial passenger jet aircraft cruises at an altitude between 30,000 and 42,000 feet. The journey is a straight air line. Like a bee line.

"Apparent" Ecliptic

The ecliptic (great circle) is not an apparent path of the sun. God is real and His creation is real. God did not make His creation to look "apparent" to earth dwellers. The ecliptic is not an apparent path of the sun among the stars over the course of a year. The path is not "apparent" because the sun moves. We can observe the motion of the sun as we live on a non-moving Earth. The sun orbits the non-moving Earth over the course of a day. We see the sun make an arc in the sky from east to west. The psalmist tells us that the sun's rising is from the end of the heavens, and its circuit to the end of them (Psalm 19:6). This is real movement, not apparent. From the Northern Hemisphere, the ecliptic arc appears high in the sky in the summer and appears closer to the horizon in the winter. It's a matter of perspective. From man's vantage point on Earth, the 12 constellations of the Zodiac arc is the sun's ecliptic path. At night time, when you look in the direction that the sun had traveled earlier that day you will see the constellations of the Zodiac or ecliptic.

"Apparent" Level

There is no difference between true and "apparent" sea level. It is what it is - level. The sea is true level, not apparent level. If there is a globular shape of the Earth, then the curvature of the Earth is the true level. Sea water on a curved earth would need to be perpendicular to stay in place. All the water in the oceans would have to be curved or bent, which is absolutely impossible if water seeks it own level. Water runs downhill to seek its own level. Gravity does not hold all the water in the seas within their God commanded boundaries. In Job 38:11 God declared to the seas He created: "You may come this far, but no further." The oceans contain 352 quintillion gallons of water. If gravity is actually powerful enough to hold sea water in its place on a round globe rotating at 1,038 mph, then why can't it hold water in a fifty-gallon barrel in place turned upside down? Or a swimming pool turned on its side? Water doesn't work that way. It runs downhill to seek it own level all over the world. Water is water. H2O is water in the seas and in a barrel and pool.

Water staying calm in the seas while the earth is rotating at 1,038 mph on a tilted axis defies the law of inertia and centrifugal force. Sea water that does not maintain a level surface while rotating at 1,038 mph and staying within its boundaries is not feasible. Take time to think that through.

Law of Inertia

Inertia is the resistance of any physical object to any charge in its velocity. This includes changes to the object's speed, or direction of motion.

If the globe is spinning at 1,038 mph, how can the water in all the oceans stay in the boundaries within their shorelines? It's not practically or physically feasible. How can anything on Earth stay in place spinning at 1,038 mph?

Convex Surface

If the Earth is a globe, there cannot be a question, however irregular the land may be in form, the water must have a convex surface. Water doesn't work that way.

The surface of standing water is not convex, therefore, the Earth is not a globe. On the contrary, the surface of water is parallel to the line-of-sight, and is therefore horizontal. Earth cannot be other than A PLANE.

If the Earth's surface were convex, the observer, looking down from a balloon or helicopter, instead of seeing it gradually ascend to eye level, would have to look downwards to the horizon and the amount of dip in the line-of-sight would become greater the higher the elevation. The Earth, taken as a whole, its land and water together, is not a globe. There is no degree of spherical shape. Water and land look level when looking downwards from a balloon, helicopter or airplane window. Water level is not apparent; it is real.

State of Kansas

Researchers have determined that the state of Kansas is indeed flatter than a pancake. Not as flat as a pancake, but actually flatter. This is disputed in Kansas. A survey revealed that more Kansans (32.5%) think it is flatter, and less think it is not (29%). Nevertheless, it is a flat state.

Discover Kansas on National Pancake Day - September 26. Fire up the griddle and make breakfast for the family.

On The Level

A rising tide lifts all boats. Water always remains level and flat according to physics and by observation. Oceans do not curve or bend because water does not curve or bend. Water remains level during a raising tide. Why is water always level? Pascal's principle: pressure is uniformly transmitted throughout the liquid.

The vast amount of water in the seven oceans is always level, not curved or bent. The water in the seas, lakes, rivers, streams, canals, ponds, water wells, reservoirs, mud puddles, bathtubs, glass, cup, kitchen sink, clear tubing, and toilet bowl is always level. How can anything remain level if we live on a spinning sphere? Impossible. If the Earth was spinning at 1,038 mph, as evolutionists claim, centrifugal force, which acts outward on the body of water, then the body's inertia would cause the ocean water to splash off the surface and out into space. In fact, nothing would remain on Earth at that speed. Bye-bye toupee. Evolutionists and heliocentrists are not on the level. Earth is not a globe. It is a flat plane.

Earth is Like a Pizza

1. A pizza has a crust. Earth has a crust. The average thickness of Earth's crust is about nine miles to 12 miles.
2. A pizza is a flat pie. Earth is a flat plane.
3. A pizza shape is a round, flat pie with a diameter ranging from 8" to 18." Earth's shape is a round, flat plane with a diameter ranging around 8,000 miles.
4. A pizza has a rim around the outer edge to keep all the ingredients on the flat pie - sauce and toppings.
    Earth has a rim around the outer edge to keep the ocean water on the flat plane. There is a 200 feet solid high ice wall all the way around the diameter of the Earth. 360o around the rim.
5. If you want it to snow on your pizza, sprinkle some Parmigiano cheese on it.

EXTRA: Why do box companies manufacture square pizza boxes and not round boxes? Because it's less expensive to make a square box.

The Earth is a Plane

The Earth is not a globe. Earth is a circle, not a sphere. The earth is a like a big bowl with a curved glass lid on top. The earth is a flat plane, without orbital or axial motion. The Flat Earth sets on a flat non-moving stationary foundation (1 Samuel 2:8; 1 Chronicles 16:30; Psalm 93:1; Psalm 96: 9-11).

All the continents center around the North Pole and are surrounded by Ocean. The South Pole does not exist. Antarctica is not a continent. No people live on Antarctica. Surrounding the flat earth 360° on all sides is Antarctica. It is also known as the Antarctic ice wall and has been measured at 200 feet high and thousands of miles long. Captain Cook sailed along the ice wall for 60,000 miles and never found an inlet.

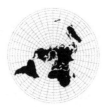

THE ANTARCTIC TREATY

Antarctica is Earth's only continent without a native human population. The Antarctic Treaty system regulates international relations with respect to Antarctica, which was signed in 1959. The Antarctic Treaty was signed by 12 countries who had scientists in and around Antarctica at the time. The entire continent is set aside as a scientific preserve. There are many rich resources in Antarctica.

The military keeps people from exploring Antarctica; from drilling for oil, digging for coal, and mining for minerals. Man is a natural born explorer. Mankind likes to discover new territory and subdue it, as God commanded in the Cultural Mandate in Genesis 1:28.

End of the Earth

Is there an end of the Earth? Yes. The Bible uses the phrase "the end of the earth" 28 times. Daniel 4:11 says a large and strong tree was visible to the ends of the earth. Jesus told His disciples in Acts 1:8 that they will be His witnesses everywhere, and to the ends of the earth. Revelation 7:1 and 20:8 refer to the four corners of the earth. Thayer's Lexicon says this means "the four extreme limits of the earth."

Antarctic is the 200 feet high ice wall around the rim of the earth. What are they trying to hide at the Antarctic? The reason for the Antarctic Treaty is to keep people from knowing that the earth has an end.

Admiral Richard E. Byrd's Encounter In Antarctica

Admiral Richard E. Byrd was one of the pioneers who traveled to the frozen wasteland of Antarctica, a barren world of deep cold.

During his Arctic flight of 1,700 miles BEYOND the North Pole he reported by radio that he saw below him, not ice and snow, but land areas consisting of mountains, forests, green vegetation, lakes and rivers, and in the underbrush saw a strange animal resembling the mammoth..."

Admiral Byrd said in February, 1947 before his North Pole flight, "I'd like to see that land beyond the Pole. That area beyond the Pole is the center of the great unknown." In January, 1956, Admiral Byrd led another expedition to the Antarctic and penetrated about 2,300 miles. Byrd said on March 13, 1956, "The present expedition has opened up a vast new land."

Solar Energy

The sun is electromagnetic power. It sends electricity to earth. That's why solar panels work. The sun produces light, heat and energy. Plants use sunlight to synthesize foods from carbon dioxide and water. This is called photosynthesis. The sun is a disc, not a ball. It is closer to the earth than evolutionists claim. The sun is a huge heat lamp that shines an isolated sun spot somewhere on earth. The sun is 34 miles across and 3,100 miles above the earth.

The Heliocentric Nonsensical Model

There is zero scientific evidence for the Heliocentric Model. It is nonsensical to believe the earth orbits the sun. This model is both unscientific and unbiblical. Capricious denied what the Bible teaches about the earth. The Heliocentric Model contradicts what the Word of God says about the nonmoving earth. The sun moves. That's why God stopped the sun for Joshua because it was actually moving. It was not an apparent movement. The sun orbits the earth every 24 hours. The earth does not move. The earth is fixed. The earth does not spin at 1,038 mph. The earth is not tilted on an axis. The North Pole is the center of the earth.

No Conflict Between Plain Science and the Bible

There is no fence between true science and the Bible. It's all one connected field growing a good crop of Truth.

To suggest that Isaiah 40:22 supports the Heliocentric theory is a misinterpretation and misapplication of the text. Nowhere does the Bible teach the Heliocentric theory. It is a false teaching filled with nonsense.

Where does the Bible say the Earth is tilted on an axis? Why would God create a tilted earth? To cause the four seasons? No! We enjoy four seasons on Earth because God created them (Genesis 1:14-19; 8:22). To claim Earth is tilted on an axis is another evolutionary lie to explain something that is not real.

Why don't we feel the Earth spinning? Grease? What about the friction at 1,038 mph? Does the grease help Earth spin smoothly? What are the name of the angels that grease the axis on the spinning earth? Are there North Pole grease angels and South Pole grease angels? Where do the angels get the grease? Do their wings get greasy smudge marks? Do they wash up in heaven or on earth? What is the diameter of the steel axis passing through the center of the spinning ball earth? BTW: These ideas are the nonsensical model.

There are no stars in the sky that are more than 6,000 miles above the Earth. There are no stars or planets that are millions of light years away from earth. That's a man-made evolutionary lie. The sky or dome is around 6,000 miles above the fixed/flat surface of the Earth. When you look up and see the sky, you are looking at a distance of 6,000 miles. When Yahweh looks down at us from the other side of the vault that He hammered out, He sees us as grasshoppers. How big is God? He's big enough to rule the universe.

Where does the Bible say other planets are tilted on an axis? To claim that we live on a tilted Earth spinning on an axis is a false image of the Earth that Elohim created in Genesis 1:1. To claim that there are photos taken of earth and other planets by a space rover is another lie from NASA. There are no actual photos of spherical planets spinning in space. What are they then? They are computer graphic images (CGI) that have been photo shopped to look real, but it's all more fake news. Have you been deceived to believe the lie?

If you have not taken the time to conduct a careful study of the Geocentric Model, you don't know what you don't know. If you have not taken the time to conduct a careful study of the Flat Earth Model, you don't know what you don't know. All you are left to do is to repeat the babel of pseudoscience nonsense and call people names.

NASA Lies

Some of NASA's launches are holograms. Fake. Holography is a method of generating three-dimensional images. Green screens are used inside studio space capsules to simulate weightlessness. Astronauts do their flips on wires to appear weightless. You can't see the wires holding them suspended in the air.

Pictures of Mars are fake. A picture of land in Greenland has been doctored to look like Mars, barren with a cloudless sky.

The History of Discoveries

The ice wall was discovered in 1946. The firmament was discovered in 1958. NASA was created in 1958 by Von Braun, a Nazi rocket scientist from Germany. The firmament is the Van Allen Radiation Belt. A powerful no go zone. The Antarctica Treaty was established in 1959 to guard the firmament. In 1962 Operation Fishbowl bombed the firmament attempting to break the glass ceiling or blow a hole in the firmament.

The Ice Wall

The ice wall is the earth's shore line. The ice wall encircles a giant lake. The flat earth is a big bowl filled with water and land with a dome on top. All of the land on earth is surrounded by water. The container for the water in Antarctica. We live in the Antarctic basin. Antarctica is not an island at the bottom of the earth. There is no South Pole. There is no bottom of the earth. Earth is not larger at the equator and smaller at the top and bottom. The earth is not a round ball. It is flat.

Beyond the Ice Wall

There are oceans and land beyond the ice wall which surround our earth. This is extra land or extra territory beyond the ice wall. This is known as extraterrestrial. A 1000 year old map was discovered in Japan with the flat earth in the center and extraterrestrial water and land beyond the ice wall. The Hawaiian Gazette headline. Was This Map Made Ten Centuries Ago? It was found in a Buddhist Temple in the mountains of central Japan. It is a map made 1000 years ago by Chinese priests ten centuries ago.

Antarctica Is Off Limits

No one is allowed to visit the Antarctic. It is off-limits. The government blocks anyone who attempts to visit the Antarctic. Guided tours are given to a limited area of Antarctica. What are they hiding? They don't want people to know that there are ends to the earth.

Daylight Saving Time

DST is fake time. It puts the sun off by one hour.

Georgia Guidestones

The Georgia Guidestones are a granite monument erected in 1980 in Elbert County, Georgia. A set of ten guidelines is inscribed on the structure in eight modern languages. The instructions for the creation of the monument were complicated. An astronomer was employed, ensuring the correct construction. The center stone has an eye-level, oblique hole drilled so that the North Star is always visible alongside a slot which is always aligned with the Sun's solstices and equinoxes. This is proof that the earth does not move. Meanwhile, the four large upright wing slabs are oriented to the limits of moon migration during the year.

The Blue Marble

We live in a make-believe world that has been foisted on us. The image of the ball earth is a photo shop image designed by NASA. The image of earth is a painting. There are no photos of the earth. The clouds are painted on the image. NASA has many images of the earth. They are all different.

What Is A Plane?

A plane is a flat surface with no thickness. Earth is a flat plane. There are only two dimensions on a plane: length and width.

God's Time Piece in Earth's System

The sky is a perfect clock. The sun orbits the earth every 24 hours. The moon orbits the earth every 28 days +/-. The sun keeps track of the hours and the days. The moon keeps track of the weeks and months. The star constellations go around the earth and measure the seasons and the years. God runs a tight ship in the universe (Ecclesiastes 3:14-16). God, who is unseen, actively guides and is deeply involved in the working of His creation. God numbered the stars and knows them all by name. When a star does not obey the Master's voice and does not do what it is commanded to do, God causes that star to fall out of the sky.

The Human Race

"And he made from one man (Adam) (one blood) every nation of mankind to live on all the face (flat) of the earth, having determined allotted periods and the boundaries of their dwelling place."
Acts 17:26

There is only one race - the human race. We all come from one blood - the same gene pool - Adam and Eve. There are many ethnic groups, but only one race. There is only one skin color - brown. There aren't any red or yellow or black or white skinned people. Only brown: light brown, middle brown, and dark brown. We're all a part of Adam's race and members of the brown family. To become a member of the family of God, a person must become a co-heir/joint-heir with Jesus Christ (Romans 8:17; 1 Peter 1:4; Galatians 4:5-7). He adopts us into His forever family (Ephesians 1:5).

Melanin is a natural brownish skin pigment. Skin, hair, and eye color in people depends on the type and amount of melanin they have in their skin cells. The more melanin the darker brown the skin. We should not judge another person based on the color of his or her skin. Rather, we judge a person by the content of their character. Character is what counts.

God determined the boundaries of nations. The Antarctic Treaty blocked man from exploring and subduing this rich pristine area.

Set Shoreline
God set boundaries for the oceans. He made the clouds its garment. He told the sea, this far shall you come, and no further (Job 38:8-11).

Form and Magnitude of the Earth
The surface of all the waters on the earth is horizontal. The ocean is one continuous body of water separated by various land mass. All the land mass of the continents is connected either above or under water. Its surface seeks the same level throughout the world. We have sea level, not sea curve. The whole mass, the land and water together, constitutes an immense non-moving circular plane.

Globalism
Does globalism exist? No, because the Earth is not a globe. Does worldwide exist? Yes, because Earth is a flat plane. Globalism should become global-wasim.

Polaris
The northern central star called "Polaris" does not move. If we travel by land or by sea towards the northern central star we come to a region of ice. The northern star is our guide. When directly above us, we are at the North Pole. Earth is suspended in space by electromagnetic power between the North Pole and Polaris. This region is THE CENTER OF THE EARTH. It is a vast central tidal sea, nearly 1,000 miles in diameter, and surrounded by a great wall or barrier of ice, 80 to 100 miles in breath.

The North Pole region is really THE CENTER OF THE EARTH. Look at the center of the NEW STANDARD MAP OF THE WORLD.

The "Tropic of Cancer" is the most northerly circle of latitude on Earth at which the Sun can be directly overhead. The meridian is the great circle passing through the celestial poles.

The Compass
A compass is one of the oldest navigational tools in history. Essentially a compass is a light weight magnet, generally a magnetized needle, on a free rotating pivot. A compass works by detecting the Earth's natural magnetic fields. The needle is

attracted to the Earth's natural magnetic north pole in the center of the Earth. Look at the center of the NEW STANDARD MAP OF THE WORLD.

The compass came into common use in the West during the 14th century AD. This led to the Age of Exploration where major European powers started further exploration of the World including North and South America. The compass brought about the golden age of exploration.

One Center

There is one center - the North. There is one circumference - the South. The Southern Region is a vast circle, and not a pole or center.

EARTH IS
AN EXTENDED PLANE

The Bible tells us: Earth is stretched out upon the waters. Earth is founded on the seas and established on the floods. Earth is standing in the water and out of the water. The depth and extent of the "mighty waters" have no limit. They constitute the "World without end."

There is direct and special evidence that the surface of the earth is not convex, but, on the contrary, a vast and irregular plane.

The Vault of Heaven

On the second day, a vault was created to divide the waters, some were above and some were below the vault. On the fourth day the sun, moon, and stars were created, and placed "in" (not above) the vault. They are free orbiting stars, not attached to the vault of heaven. The word "vault" is used 17 times in the OT texts. In each usage it is translated from the Hebrew word raqiya, which means the visible vault of the sky, or a space or firmament or vault or sky or heaven (depending on the translation). The word raqiya comes from riqqua, which means "beaten out." In ancient times, brass objects were beaten into shape on an anvil. A good craftsman could beat a lump of cast brass into a thin bowl. In Job 37, Elihu proclaimed God's majesty. Elihu asked Job, "Can you beat out [raqa] the vault of the skies, as he does, hard as a mirror of cast metal?" (Job 37:18)

Elihu's question shows that the Hebrews considered the vault of heaven a solid, physical object. Such a large dome would be a tremendous feat of engineering. The Hebrews (and Yahweh Himself) considered it exactly that, and this point is hammered home by five scriptures.

> "...who alone stretched out the heavens [shamayim]..."
> *Job 9:8*

> "The heavens [shamayim] tell out the glory of God,
> the vault of heaven [raqiya] reveals his handiwork."
> *Psalm 19:1*

> "...the heavens [shamayim] are the work of your hands."
> *Psalm 102:25*

> "I made the earth and created man on it; it was my hands
> that stretched out the heavens, [shamayim]
> and caused all their host to shine..."
> *Isaiah 45:12*

> "My hand laid the foundation of the earth,
> and my right hand spread out the heavens [shamayim]..."
> *Isaiah 48:13*

These verses are not about a mere illusion of a vault. Shamayim comes from shameh, a root meaning to be lofty. It literally means the sky. Shamayim means heavens. The Hebrew ending im is plural.

Other passages paint the picture of the sky as a lofty, physical dome. God "sits enthroned on the vaulted roof of earth [chuwg], whose inhabitants are like grasshoppers. He stretches out the skies [shamayim] like a curtain, he spreads them out like a tent to live in... (Isaiah 40:22)." Chuwg literally means "circle" or "encompassed." It can mean roundness, as in a rounded dome or vault. Job 22:14 says God "walks to and fro on the vault of heaven [chuwg]." In both verses, the use of chuwg implies a physical object, on which one can sit and walk. Likewise, the context in both cases requires elevation. In Isaiah, the elevation causes the people below to look as small as grasshoppers. In Job, God's eyes must penetrate the clouds to view the doings of humans below. Elevation is also implied by Job 22:12: "Surely God is at the zenith of the heavens [shamayim] and looks down on all the stars, how lofty they are!"

The Hebrew word raqiya is used five times in Ezekiel, four times in Ezekiel 1:22-26 and once in Ezekiel 10:1. In each case the context requires a literal vault or dome. The vault appears above the "living creatures" and glitters "like a sheet of ice." Above the vault is a throne of sapphire. Seated on the throne is "a form in human likeness," which is radiant and "like the appearance of the glory of the Lord." In short, Ezekiel saw a vision of God sitting enthroned on the vault of heaven, as described in Isaiah 40:22.

The River of Life

"Then the angel showed me the river of the water of life, bright as crystal, flowing from the throne of God and of the Lamb through the middle of the street of the city; also, on either side of the river, the tree of life with its twelve kinds of fruit, yielding its fruit each month. The leaves of the tree were for the healing of the nations. No longer will there be anything accursed, but the throne of God and of the Lamb will be in it, and his servants will worship him. They will see his face, and his name will be on their foreheads. And night will be no more. They will need no light of lamp or sun, for the Lord God will be their light, and they will reign forever and ever."
Revelation 22:1-5 ESV

The Dome

The earth's sky is surrounded by a sky dome that holds in the air and protects us. We live in an enclosed system. Everything on earth is under the hardened glass dome. The firmament is a glass circular disc in the shape of a dome sitting on top of the flat Earth. It's like a glass lid on top of a bowl filled with water. You can see through the dome. The Bible says it is made of hardened glass, as hard as a cast metal mirror (Job 37:18). It's called the glass dome or glass ceiling. The firmament is firm. It separates water from water. The Bible clearly describes a firm dome (firmament) in which the sun and moon and stars were placed on the fourth day (Genesis 1:14-19). Somewhere beyond the ice wall, the dome rests over the earth. The stars are contained under the dome. The dome does not turn each day. It's fixed. The motion of stars that we see each night are circling above the earth. The stars motion is not produced by a turning dome.

The Bible describes how the wise men saw a moving star as a sign of the birth of the King of the Jews. When they saw the star, they rejoiced with exceeding great joy. The text in Matthew 2, tells us that the wise men "saw his star when it rose" and followed it to Jerusalem and then on to Bethlehem. It is true that the star in heaven moved with the wise men up to the place of the birth of Jesus. This was God's original GPS system.

Throne of God

God's throne is located in the third heaven above the firmament, or dome. Revelation 4:6-9 says before the throne there was a sea of glass like crystal. The sea of glass is the expanse or firmament. It sits just above the sky. Look up! God is right on the other side of the big blue sky that He created on the second day of creation week. God called the expanse Heaven (Genesis 1:6-8).

God can see the whole earth from His vantage point in the third heaven. "For the eyes of the LORD run to and fro throughout the whole earth" (2 Chronicles 16:9a). Hebrews 4:13 says, "Nothing in all creation is hidden from God's sight."

Ezekiel 10:1 says, "Then I looked, and behold, on the expanse that was over the heads of the cherubim (plural; winged angelic beings that attend God) there appeared above them something like a sapphire (gleaming metal), in appearance like a throne."

Grasshoppers

Isaiah 40:22 says that God sits enthroned above the circle of the earth. That's above the firmament; the curved glass dome or sky. Isaiah 40:22 is sometimes called the "grasshopper" verse. But that's not what this verse is about. Some quote it as evidence for the sphericity of the earth. Quoting the King James version "he sitteth upon the circle of the earth" the late Dr. Henry M. Morris, in his book, The Bible and Modern Science, ignored the context and the grasshoppers and claimed "circle" should read "sphericity" or "roundness." This is poor scholarship. Morris was wrong.

This verse is referring to the dome shaped expanse. God sits enthroned above the dome. What do people on earth look like to God from the circle? Like grasshoppers. This is a figure of speech; a simile. From God's perspective, people look as small as grasshoppers. God spreads out the heavens like a curtain or canopy and makes His tent from them. A tent is always set up on a flat surface, not a round ball. God dwells in the tent He made from the stretched out heavens.

Operation Fishbowl (1962)

Are we living in a fishbowl? Operation Fishbowl was a series of high altitude nuclear tests in 1962 that were carried out by the United States as a part of the larger Operation Dominic atmospheric nuclear test program.

Operation Dominic was a series of 31 nuclear test explosions with a 38. Mt (159 PJ) total yield conducted in 1962 by the United States in the Pacific. These shots were collectively called Operation Fishbowl.

They set up a row of rockets with instruments for making scientific measurements of high-altitude nuclear tests. All of the tests were launched on missiles from Johnston Island in the Pacific Ocean north of the equator. These rockets were said to be hitting the Glass Ceiling / Dome which is our electromagnetic field (in layman's terms: "the Van Allen Radiation Belt").

Dominic Chama

From the Latin dominicus meaning "pertaining to the Lord." Dominic means "of the Lord." Chama means: a fixed massive irregular nonequivalent shell; the shell belonging to God. Operation Fishbowl was to test the fishbowl of the Lord.

In 1962, the rocket scientists knew the earth was a flat plane with a dome on top. In their arrogance, they thought the missiles were powerful enough to break through God's glass ceiling.

The missiles loaded with nuclear weapons hit the sky dome and exploded into huge mushroom fireballs, one after another. The bright mushroom cloud reflected off the glass dome and could be seen in the other hemisphere.

> The One enthroned in heaven laughs.
> The Lord scoffs at them.
> *Psalm 2:4*

THE CELESTIAL BODIES

The Hebrews considered the celestial bodies relatively small. The Genesis creation account indicates the size and importance of the earth relative to the celestial bodies in two ways, first by their order of creation, and second by their positional relationships. They had to be small to fit inside the vault of heaven. The cosmos is not expanding. God completed creating in Genesis 2:1. The stars are not millions of light years away. A light year is the distance that light travels in one year at 186,000 miles per second. Evolution says bigger is expanding, plus time and chance. Creation says small works best. Small size is implied by Joshua 10:12, which says that the sun stood still "in Gibeon" and the moon "in the Valley of Aijalon." Two local isolated hotspots.

The Bible often presents celestial bodies as exotic living beings. For example, the sun in Psalm 19 is portrayed as a bridegroom. "In them [the heavens], a tent is fixed for the sun, who comes out like a bridegroom from his wedding canopy, rejoicing like a strong man to run his race. His rising is at one end of the heavens, his circuit touches their farthest ends; and nothing is hidden from his heat (Psalm 19:4-6)." This passage is about the sun orbiting the earth from sunrise to sunset; from east to west.

The stars are anthropomorphic demigods. When the earth's cornerstone was laid "the morning stars sang together and all the sons of God shouted aloud" (Job 38:7). The morning star (Lucifer, Isaiah 14:12) is censured for trying to set his throne above that of other stars: You thought in your own mind, I will scale the heavens; I will set my throne high above the stars of God, I will sit on the mountain where the gods meet in the far recesses of the north. I will rise high above the cloud-banks and make myself like the most high (Isaiah 14:13-14).

Deuteronomy 4:15-19 recognizes the god-like status of stars, noting that they were created for other people to worship. Stars can fall from the skies according to Daniel 8:10 and Matthew 24:29. The same idea is found in the following passages from Revelation 6:13-16:...the stars in the sky fell to the earth, like figs shaken down by a gale; the sky vanished, as a scroll is rolled up...they called out to the mountains and the crags, "Fall on us and hide us from the face of the One who sits on the throne..." This is consistent with the Hebrew cosmology. The writer considered the stars small objects, all of which could fall to the earth without eliminating human life. He also viewed the sky as a physical object. The stars are inside the sky, and they fall. When it is whisked away, it reveals the One enthroned above (see Isaiah 40:22).

The Law of Perspective

The true law of perspective, which is, that parallel lines appear in the distance to converge (meet) to one and the same data point line.

First, if the hull of an outbound ship on the water disappears before the mast head, the water is convex, and therefore the earth is a globe. Such a phenomenon can only result from a convex surface. This is erroneous. The Earth and water are not convex or round. Water does not curve. Water seeks it own level.

The Seven Seas include: the Arctic, North Atlantic, South Atlantic, North Pacific, South Pacific, Indian, and Southern Oceans. They are all at sea level all the time. Ships don't disappear over the horizon. Our eyesight is limited. The ship can be brought back into view with a camera zoom lens or powerful telescope.

Second, if we were to observe miles of a parallel railroad track that is straight and level, in the distance, they appear to come together. They appear to join together in the distance. But they do not. It's a matter of perspective.

If an observer stood on the shoreline of the ocean with his eye line at an elevation of six feet above the water, and watched a ship until it is "hull down," then looked through a telescope with power enough to magnify at the surface or vanishing point, the hull would be visibly restored to sight. The conclusion of the experiment shows that it had disappeared through the influence of perspective, not from having sunk behind the peak of a convex surface. You cannot look through the mass of water with a telescope, or look over its surface and down the other side.

Due East and West

What is meant by sailing due east and west? It is sailing at right angles to north and south. This is determined by the mariners' compass. Sailing toward the center of the Earth is sailing north. Sailing away from the center of the Earth is sailing south. Looking at the NEW STANDARD MAP OF THE WORLD gives a proper perspective.

Polaris, the North Star sets at the end of the handle of the Little Dipper. Polaris does not move, but remains in the same spot above the northern horizon year-round while the other stars circle around it. The star has been seen from many degrees beyond the equator. This is an important argument against the doctrine of the Earth's rotundity or that it is a globe.

The whole extent of Earth's circumference is an arithmetic question. What is the distance made by 360° into which the surface is divided? The answer: 22,657 nautical miles; or, 8,357 nautical miles more than the theory of rotundity would permit.

Railroads and Canals

When laying out railways and canals surveyors used to allow eight inches per mile in construction for the Earth's curvature. The surface would stand eight inches higher in the middle than at the ends. In regard to both railroads and canals, whenever the eight inch allowance was attempted the work was not satisfactory. The results were so irregular in the early days of building rail roads, canals, and other surveying projects, most distinguished engineers stopped the practice of the old "forward leveling" which allowed for convexity (contour), and adapted the "back-and-fore sight" method. Just eyeball it. It was considered that whether the surface was convex or horizontal it would be of no consequence in practice if the bubble level or theodolite were employed to read both forwards and backwards. A theodolite is a precision optical surveying instrument with a rotating telescope for measuring horizontal and vertical angles. The Ordinance Department of the Government made the forsaking of all ideas of rotundity compulsory. This bad scientific idea was the product of Darwinian evolution and Copernican heliocentrism. It is evident that the doctrine of Earth's rotundity or globe cannot be mixed up with the practical operations of civil engineers and surveyors. This was a foolish idea that wasted time and destroyed property. These designers followed the thinking of some who were determined to involve the global Earth model in their calculations, even if it did not work. The convexity of the Earth's surface is a myth. It's the result of brainwashing and indoctrination.

The government was obligated to interfere. Now every survey, whether by ordinance or otherwise, is carried out based on horizontal information. No other method proved satisfactory. This is virtually an admission by all honest scientific men that the Earth cannot be other than a flat plane.

Remember the lyrics in My Fair Lady. The flower girl Eliza Dolittle sings: The rain in Spain stays mainly in the plain.

No matter where it's raining in the world, the rain stays in the plane because the Earth is a flat plane and the rainwater seeks its own level.

The Shape of the Earth

The necessary flatness of the earth's surface is required by verses like Daniel 4:10-11. In Daniel, the king "saw a tree of enormous height in the middle of the land... the tree grew large and strong and its top touched the sky; it was visible to the ends of the earth." If the earth were not flat, an enormously tall tree would not be visible to "the ends of the earth," because this is impossible on a spherical earth. Likewise, in describing the temptation of Jesus by Satan, Matthew 4:8 says, "Once again, the devil took him to a very high mountain, and showed him all the kingdoms of the world [cosmos] in their glory." Obviously, this would be possible only if the earth were flat. The same is true of Revelation 1:7: "Behold, he is coming with the clouds, and every eye will see him..."

Those who hold that the Earth is a globe claim that in the eclipse of the Moon there is proof of rotundity. That the shadow of the Earth on the Moon is always round, and that nothing but a globe could cast a circular shadow. But it has not been proved that the Moon is eclipsed by a shadow. It has not been proved that the Earth moves in an orbit. It has not been proved that the Moon receives its light from the Sun.

The Earth has no motion in space. Earth is not tilted on an axis. The Moon is not a reflector of the Sun's light. It is self-luminous. Luminary means: source of light. The Moon is not a reflector. Genesis 1:16 says, "God made two great lights." Two lights: Sun and Moon. God created two lights on Day Four of creation week. The Sun is the greater light that rules the day. The Moon is the lesser light that rules the night. The same Hebrew word for light (hammeorot) is used for both the Sun and the Moon. Both are lights

THE SUN MOVES

We say: sun's orbit, sun is orbiting, sunspot, isolated sunspot, sunrise, sunset, sunshine, sunlight, sunny day, rising, risen, arise, arose, rose, sun rising, sun setting, went down, going down, down, go down, up, sun up to sunset, high noon, gone down, went down, dusk, dawn, crack of dawn, twilight, beyond the sunset, "sun, stand still." Somewhere the sun is always shinning.

Distance of the Sun and the Moon

If the altitude of the Sun at high noon is measured from two stations on the same elevation of similar height at the same hour, and the length of the base line is determined, the difference in the Sun's altitude is the distance in the side of a triangle. The base is the Earth's surface, and the vertical side the zenith distance of the Sun. This is called triangulation. The calculation made from these elements gives the result, that the actual distance of the Sun from the Earth is 3,100 miles. Not 93 million miles, as Darwinian evolutionists claim. The Sun and the Moon are the same size. Using the same method of measuring distances applies equally to the Stars. All the visible objects in the firmament are contained within the distance of 6,000 miles. From demonstrable distances it is shown that the magnitude of the Sun, Moon, and Stars is small - much smaller than the Earth from which they are measured. They are secondary and subservient.

The Heliocentric Sun

From earth, it seems like we are standing still, and we are. We don't feel like we're hurtling through space, because we are not. Yet, secular science tells us Earth is moving around the sun. Biblical creation tells us we live in a geocentric universe in which Earth lies at the center of everything. We live on a non-moving earth. The sun rotates parallel above us. As everyone observes, the sun rises and the sun sets every 24 hours.

Secular science says the sun revolves around the center of the Milky Way galaxy - a cosmic year. Not true. The sun's orbit is limited to the sky above the earth. God created the sun to light the earth for man, not wander around the Milky Way galaxy. At the same time, secular science says, Earth revolves (orbits) around the sun while spinning at 1,038 mph. Two spins. Secular science says the time it takes for the Earth to go around the Sun is one year. A bullet travels more than 2,600 feet per second, or over 1,800 mph. Bullets travel over twice the speed of sound. Secular science says earth's average orbital speed is about 19 miles per second, or 67,000 miles per hour. That's practically impossible. Absolutely not true.

The Sun Moves in a Circle Over the Earth

There is no scientific support for a heliocentric model of the solar system. The Earth does revolve around the Sun. The flat Earth model places Earth at the center of the cosmos. The Sun circles over the top side of the world like a carousel, broadcasting light and warmth downward like a desk lamp. The Sun moves in an arc and returns to the center of the arc completing a circle. The Sun does this daily and visibly. Read what the Bible says about the path of the Sun.

> The heavens proclaim the glory of God.
> The skies display his craftsmanship.
> Day after day they continue to speak;
> night after night they make him known.
> They speak without a sound or word;
> their voice is never heard.
> Yet their message has gone throughout the earth,

and their words to all the world.
God has made a home in the heavens for the sun.
It bursts forth like a radiant bridegroom after his wedding.
It rejoices like a great athlete eager to run the race.
The sun rises at one end of the heavens
and follows its course to the other end.
Nothing can hide from its heat.
Psalm 19:1-6 NLT

Edwin Hubble

There is real evidence of the dome. Edwin Hubble admitted in his book, The Observational Approach to Cosmology, that the observable Cosmos was small and curved all around us like a sky dome. He did not and could not explain it. He ignored it as he did the evidence for Geocentrism.

The Map of the Earth

The map of the earth is technically known as an azimuthal equidistant projection. The North Pole is positioned at the center, and the map does not have a south pole.

Creation Completed

Genesis 2:1 tells us: "Thus the heavens and the earth were completed in all their vast array." The earth is not continually expanding, as evolutionists claim. Genesis 2:1 states that the creation of the heavens and the earth and everything in them was completed. It is complete. God did not say to Adam one day during the second week, "Oh! I forgot to make dinosaurs! Give me 17 minutes." No, according John 1:1-3, God had all of His work of creation planned out in His mind before He began to create on that first Sunday in October of 4004 BC.

On the seventh day God had finished His work of creation, so He rested from all His work. God started His work of creation on Sunday and completed it on Friday and then rested on Saturday. He blessed the seventh day and declared it holy (Genesis 2:2-3). The Jewish Sabbath (Hebrew shavat: "to rest"). The cosmos is the same size today as the day God completed His creative work. It is not expanding.

The Sun's Path

The Bible clearly teaches that the Earth was created before the Sun. The sun is not fixed. The motion of the sun is a visible reality (Psalm 19:4b-6). It is not an illusion. It is not apparent motion. It is real. The subject of Psalm 19:4-6 is the path the sun takes. The measuring line is the route the sun takes. The circuit is the path the sun takes. The sun comes out like a bridegroom leaving his chamber in the morning. He's moving.

Perspective produces the rising and setting of a flat-earth sun. The sun passes over the earth and returns to the same point every 24 hours. The Sun's path is nearest the North Pole in summer, and farthest away from it in winter. This difference in position is the result of the difference of altitude, as observed at various periods of the year.

The Earth is an extended plane. The distance of the sun from the Earth may be ascertained by the process of plane trigonometry. Three points: point A, point B, and an object in the sky. Both the sun and the moon are luminaries. The sun and the moon are the same size. The moon is nearer to the earth than the sun. The distance between the Earth and the Moon is not 238,855 miles, as evolutionists claim. All visible luminaries in the firmament are contained within a vertical distance of 3,100 statute miles. The sun cannot possibly be 93 million miles above earth. This is another ridiculous lie of evolution. The magnitude of the sun, moon, stars, and comets is comparatively small - much smaller than the earth from which they are measured. They are secondary and subservient. They are "centers of action," created on Day Four (Genesis 1:16), casting down light, and chemical products upon the earth. Light and heat radiate equally in all directions.

The sun, moon, and stars did not exist for the first three days of creation week. God, who is light, created them on the fourth day. They are light holders.

The sun's path is nearer the polar center in summer, and farthest away from it in winter. The sun's path gets larger every day from December 21st to June 22nd; and smaller every day from June 22nd to December 21st, of every year. The sun's annual course is demonstrable by actual observation.

The sun and moon serve mankind according to God's design. The sun and moon are both luminaries over the day and night (Psalm 136:7-9). The stars are mentioned in passing.

The sun travels around the earth on two circular paths each year. The sun is on the outer circle beginning on the 21st of December, the shortest day. On the 21st of June, the sun gradually contracts its path and arrives at the inner circle, the longest day.

If you travel far enough north, (69 degrees north latitude) you can see the sun at midnight.

The differences in the weather in the north and south could not exist if the earth were a globe, turning upon an axis underneath a non-moving sun. The peculiarities observed in the south as compared with the north, could not exist upon a globe.

They do exist, therefore the earth is not a globe.

They are such as could and must exist upon a plane.

They do exist, therefore the earth is a plane.

.

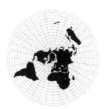

THE PURPOSE
OF THE STARS

"And God said, 'Let there be lights in the expanse of the
heavens to separate the day from the night, And let them be for
signs and for seasons, and for days and years.'"
Genesis 1:14 ESV

A Central Body

There are no fixed stars proper. This has been demonstrated by the peculiar orbital motions which those fixed stars have in addition to their daily course about the earth. Astronomers have sought in vain for a central body, the attraction of which would keep those stars in their course. But there must be such a central body, and it must be our earth. This was the conclusion attained, after the most comprehensive investigation of this problem. Dr. Alfred Russel Wallace (1823-1913) was called the "Grand Old Man" of Science. Dr. Wallace a man of acknowledged scientific ability, told the world that the earth is the center of the universe, that the earth is the only inhabited place, and that the entire creation was ordered and designed for man's sole benefit and accommodation. And corresponding to the greater formation of

135

land upon the northern hemisphere, the greater number of stars is found on the northern half of the heavens.

Location of the Stars

The KJV says, "he made the stars also." That's a pretty big also. Genesis 1:17a says, "And God set them in the expanse of the heavens to give light on the earth." God placed the stars under the dome in the second heaven as lights on the earth. Each star is a light. Each star twinkles with delight in the night. Starlight. All the stars, in harmony, rotate from east to west. Some claim that the stars are attached to the dome and the dome spins which rotates the stars. Neither the earth nor the dome spin. The earth is fixed. The Sun, the Moon, and the Stars rotate around the Earth every 24 hours. They all give their own light on earth. The Sun, the Moon, and the Stars are all self-luminaries. God made them as lights. Not one a light and one a reflector (Genesis 1:16).

Name and Number

Psalm 147:4 tells us that God determines the number of stars and calls them all by name. Name and number. Amos 5:8 says the LORD who created the stars, made the Pleiades and Orion. He turns midnight into dawn and darkens day into night.

It's A Matter of Perspective

Time-lapse camera photo's of sunsets prove that Earth is a flat plane. When the sun is closer it looks higher. When the sun is further away it looks lower. The sun looks close to us because it is. The sun looks like it is coming at us. If you walk toward a tall building, the closer you get to the building it looks taller, although it's the same height. It's a matter of perspective.

If the sun were 93 million miles away, the sunset would fade evenly across the entire horizon. But that's not the reality we observe. Sunlight shrinks and follows the sun. The sunlight shrinks as it follows the sun in the West. The whole horizon fades evenly. This would not be true if the sun were 93 million miles away. The sun swings to the right like a bowling ball. The sun is local, not 93 million miles away.

I am the LORD

> I am the LORD, and there is no other, besides me there is no
> God; I equip you though you do not know me, that people may
> know, from the rising of the sun and from the west, that there is
> none besides me; I am the LORD, and there is no other. I form
> light and create darkness, I make well-being and create calamity,
> I am the LORD, who does all these things.
> *Isaiah 45:5-7 ESV*

Isolated Sun Hotspot

Somewhere on earth there is always an isolated sun spot that is directly under the sun. As the sun moves, the hotspot moves under it. The Sun is close to the earth and its light is local. The distance between the Sun and the Earth is 3,100 miles. The Sun is 34 miles across. The Sun is a disc. It's like a ginormous heat lamp in the sky. It produces light, heat, and energy.

If the sun is 93 million miles away, there would be no isolated sun hotspots on the earth. There would be no sun rays in the clouds. The sunshine would cover the entire United States from coast to coast starting early in the day. The different time zones would not matter.

In Joshua 10, the Sun and the Moon were both moving above the Earth. Joshua asked the LORD to stop the sun in the midst of the heaven. So God commanded the Sun to stand still because it was in motion. God would not tell the sun to stand still if it was already still. No other explanation is necessary.

The earth has never moved. Never. It has always been fixed since Genesis 1:1. The sun began traveling in its orbital path above the earth on Day Four. The sun has been moving ever since.

The sun was orbiting Earth over Gibeon. The LORD commanded the sun to stand still. The result? The sun stood still. Still means: inactive, motionless, static, non-moving, unmoving. This is a geocentric passage.

Don't forget, God did not create the Sun, the Moon and the stars until the fourth day of Creation week. God, who is light (1 John 1:5), created light on the first day of Creation week (Genesis 1:3-5), but waited until the fourth day to create the light holders. For the heliocentric gang, the Earth had no sun to go around until the fourth day.

Israel needed more time to win the battle over five enemy armies. The Sun did not hurry to set for about a day. There has never been no day like it before or since. Joshua 10:12-13 tell us that the Sun stood still at Gibeon, and the Moon stopped in the Valley of Aijalon. Why name these two places? Because the Sun's isolated hotspot was over Gibeon, and the Moon's isolated beam was over the Valley of Aijalon. It was a distance of around 15 miles between Gibeon and the Valley of Aijalon. It was high noon in July.

The sun standing still account in Joshua 10 is literal history. It is not fiction. It is not a metaphor. It was not apparent. It was real. It didn't seem to happen, it happened. It was a miracle, not a mirage. It happened just the way the text reads. Nothing changed on earth that historic day except that there was more daylight. In the NT, the wind and waves obeyed the voice of Jesus (Matthew 8:27). In the OT, the Sun obeyed the command of the LORD. "Sun, stand still!" And the sun stood still, and the moon stopped. Christians who believe that the Bible is the inerrant, infallible Word of God have no problem believing in a supernatural God who intervenes in history with supernatural acts. God stopped the sun for a reason. Joshua prayed that God would help the Israelites in their battle by stopping the sun. They won!

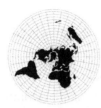

ANCIENT BOOK OF JASHER

There are 13 ancient history books that are mentioned and recommended by the Bible. The Ancient Book of Jasher is the only one of the 13 that still exists. It is referenced in Joshua 10:13; 2 Samuel 1:18; and 2 Timothy 3:8. This ancient document confirms the Scripture and the chronology given in the Hebrew version of the Old Testament.

The Book of Jasher means the Book of the Upright or the Book of the Just Man. It is a lost non-canonical book mentioned in the Hebrew Bible.

Back to the Ignorant Brethren

Most pastors of fundamentalist and evangelical churches, and teachers and professors in Christian colleges and universities today draw their knowledge of God's created universe from two opposing schools of thought: (1) The City of God; and (2) The Secular City. What they know about the Genesis creation account they got from The City of God school of thought. And what they know about the heliocentric model and the global ball earth model they got from The Secular City school of thought. They have fallen into the trap of synergism. Mixing two opposing schools of thought and calling it science. They are ignorant brethren when it comes to knowing and understanding the geocentric model and the flat earth model. Christian schools, universities, and seminaries don't deal with these topics or, if they do, they actually teach the heliocentric model and the global ball theory. Most pastors never mention these models when discussing the day the sun stood still in Joshua 10. They make excuses. They repeat the secular science they learned in school instead of studying the Scriptures for all they're worth. When God said, "Sun, stand still", the sun stopped in the sky because it was moving. 'Twas not apparent, 'twas real. You can't really understand or properly interpret Joshua 10 if you don't hold to the geocentric model. Most of the ignorant brethren deny that the sun stood still even though that's what the text clearly states. The same Bible they claim to believe about cardinal doctrines, they doubt when it says something about scientific matters. The Bible is not a book of science, but it is correct when it speaks on matters of science.

Penknife

In Jeremiah 36, we read the account of the prophet Jeremiah when he was no longer allowed to go into the LORD'S temple to speak because the people did not want to hear about all the disaster the LORD intended to bring on them for their sins and the wicked things they had done. Jeremiah hired a scribe to write down on a scroll all the LORD'S words that he told him. He was told to read aloud from the scroll where all of the people could hear him read what Jeremiah had said. They read it within the hearing of the people outside the temple as they were leaving. Then it was read to some of the nation's leaders. After they heard it, they reported it to King Jehoiakim. The king was sitting in his winter quarters in front of a fireplace. As soon as the king heard the scroll read to him he took out a penknife and cut off columns of the scroll and threw them on the fire in the firepot. He kept doing so until the whole scroll was burned up in the fire.

The sad part of this story is that neither the king nor any of the attendants showed any alarm. He ordered those who objected to the burning to be arrested. And, he ordered that the scribe Baruch and the prophet Jeremiah be arrested. However, the LORD hid them (Jeremiah 36:1-26).

Those who say they are Christian creationists and claim to believe the Bible is inspired and inerrant (without error) have in essence over the years themselves taken out their own penknife and cut out all the verses that say the Earth is not moving and that say Earth is a flat plane. Why? Because they have been indoctrinated to believe the heliocentric model and the spherical spinning earth model to be scientifically true, but neither are found in the Bible.

Why have all the fundamentalist and evangelical pastors and professors been silent? Why have elected politicians who claim to be Christians been silent? Political correctness? Cowards? Ignorant of the times? Who raised a strong objection in the public square to the Scopes Trial in 1925, or to Darwin's Origin of Species book in 1869, or to Copernicus's theory published in 1543, or to Galileo's publication of a heliocentric pamphlet in 1610, or to the Supreme Court's unprecedented and unconstitutional rulings: no prayer in 1962, no Bible reading in 1963, no posting of the 10 Commandments in 1980, abortion as a right in Roe vs. Wade in 1973, or to the LGBTQ agenda, or to gay marriage as a right protected by the US Constitution in all 50 states in 2015? The list could go on.

If Christian creationists as pastors and professors, insist that creationism is true because it's biblical, then it's inconsistent to deny that the earth is flat, doesn't move, rests on pillars, and the sun, moon, and stars revolve around it. If a Christian creationist can reject the flat earth model and/or the geocentric model, then why can't creationism also be rejected?

God is uncreated reality. He is real, not apparent. All of creation is created reality. It is real, not apparent. The miracles of Jesus were real, not apparent. He walked on water. It was not apparent. He turned water into the best wine. It was not apparent. Is John 3:16 just apparent?

There are dozens of sermons on YouTube entitled "The Day the Sun Stood Still." One pastor of a large multi-ministry church, after giving an introduction to what was leading up to Israel's battle against the five enemy armies, read Joshua 10:13. The text reads, "So the sun stood still, and the moon stopped." His next words were shocking. He said, "The earth stood still. We know the sun does not move. The earth goes around the sun and spins at 1000 mph." What? He had the audacity to change the written Word of God to the heliocentric view taught by the secular scientists in his sermon in church in front of thousands of people and many more watching on television. He chose to believe pseudoscience over Scripture. Indoctrination is a powerful method of teaching. No doubt his commentary left the people confused. Perhaps someone questioned him after the service. They should have, because he was categorically wrong.

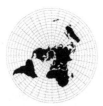

CHRISTOPHER COLUMBUS

In 1492, Columbus sailed the ocean blue.

Italian explorer Christopher Columbus set sail from Spain in three ships across the Atlantic Ocean. Columbus never set out to prove the earth was round. Superstition and ignorance caused the contemporaries of Columbus to think he would fall off the edge. His contemporaries believed the earth was flat and that one might sail off the edge. Columbus never feared sailing off the edge of the world. He was a man of faith and action. It's ironic, but more educated people now believe in a flat-earth than during Columbus's time.

The Sun Dial

God is pro-choice. King Hezekiah was offered a choice: the shadow on the sundial could go either 10 degrees backwards or 10 degrees forwards. Hezekiah thought that the sun going backward would be a greater sign since it would go against nature. God granted Isaiah's prayer and the sign happened. It was a supernatural intervention. It was not a mirage. This is the miracle that Hezekiah received (2 Kings 20:8-11).

The Talking Donkey

After the prophet Balaam started punishing the donkey he was riding for refusing to move, God miraculously gave the donkey the power to speak to Balaam

(Numbers 22:28). The donkey complained about Balaam's treatment. He beat the donkey to get back on the road. God was very angry with Balaam for meeting with the Moabite officials. The angel of the Lord stood in the road to oppose him. Balaam did not see the angel, but the donkey did. Two talking asses, one with four legs and one with two legs. Then the Lord opened Balaam's eyes, and he saw the angel of the Lord standing in the road with his sword drawn. So he bowed low and fell facedown (on the flat earth).

Balaam said, "I must speak only what God puts in my mouth"
(Numbers 22:38).

Day and Night

The period of day and night occur in every part of the Earth, except within the Arctic circle. Way up North. As the Sun moves from East to West, and completes the circle in 24 hours, it will produce in that period morning, noon, evening, and night to all parts of the Earth in succession.

During the Winter season, the shortest days, morning, noon, evening, midnight, there is six months of darkness at the Arctic circle. This constant at the pole are all a part of one general phenomenon. The Sun's path begins to diminish every day until in six months, or on the 15th of June, it is evident that the same extent of sunlight reaches over or beyond the pole, when morning, noon, evening, and night will again occur as before, but the amount of light is now much larger than when the Sun was upon the circle, and represents the longest days, or the Summer season, or six months of light at the pole. Day and night, long and short days, Winter and Summer, the long periods of alternate light and darkness at the pole, arise from the Sun's position in relation to the North Pole.

The Earth is a flat Plane, and cannot be a ball Globe.

Sunrise and Sunset

Somewhere the sun is always shining. The Sun is above and parallel to the Earth's surface at all times. It appears to ascend the firmament from morning until noon, and to descend and sink below the horizon at evening. This is because of the everywhere visible law of perspective. For example, when a balloon sails overhead without increasing or decreasing in altitude, it appears to approach the horizon gradually to the observer. In a row of street lights, the farthest light in the row appears the lowest, although each one is the same height. The Sun, although always parallel to the surface to the Earth, appears to ascend when approaching, and descend after leaving the noon-day position. "Sunrise" and "Sunset" are phenomena dependent entirely upon the fact that horizontal lines parallel to each other appear to converge in the distance. The surface of the Earth is horizontal. The Sun's path is parallel with it. This produces the observed phenomena at the line-of-sight of the observer.

Solar and Lunar Eclipses

An Eclipse of the Sun is caused by the Moon passing before it, or between it and the person observing on the Earth. The Moon is a disc, not a ball. The Moon's whole surface is brilliantly illuminated. The surface of the Moon is not illuminated from the Sun. No portion of the Moon is sunlit. If a silver glass ball is held in front of a bright light, instead of the whole surface reflecting light, there will be only a very small portion mainly in the center that is illuminated. A full Moon (maximum illumination) shines beautifully in a clear firmament; a cloudless night. The light from a full Moon glows over the edge. It's called Moon glow. There are four primary phases of the Moon: New Moon, First Quarter, Full Moon, and Last Quarter. Eight altogether.

Moon Day

The words Moon and month come from the same root. Monday gets its name from the Anglo-Saxon word "Momdamdaeg" which translates to "the moon's day." Nordic cultures worshiped the goddess of the moon.

The light of the Sun and of the Moon are different in their general appearance - in the color and action on the eyes.

The Sun's light is drying and antiseptic. The Moon's light is damp and putrefacient. It produces cold energy and a bad odor.

The Sun's rays will put out a common fire; the Moon's light will increase the combustion.

The light from the Sun shining on certain chemical substances, produces a change in color, as in photographic processes. The light from the Moon does not produce the same effect. The expression "pale cold Moon" is beautiful poetically and true philosophically.

The Moon does not have the conditions necessary for reflection. Therefore, the Moon is not a reflector, but a self-luminous body. A Lunar Eclipse does not and could not occur from a shadow of the Earth. A Solar Eclipse occurs from the Moon passing over the Sun.

A Lunar Eclipse can only occur from a similar cause. Astronomers have concluded that there may be at least one non-luminous body of large size which is attached as a satellite to this Earth.

We reject the doctrine of the Earth's rotundity and the Newtonian philosophy generally.

Forms of our Continents

The forms of our continents contradict the hypothesis of the rotation of the earth. Were there such a rotation, these formations would have been built up in the main directions, from east to west; whereas, in reality, we find their longitudinal development from north to south. The trend of continents is absolutely opposed to the theory.

Oceanography

The oceans have circulating currents or 'paths' according to Psalm 8:8 and Isaiah 43:16. The paths in the seas were created by God. Gulf Stream currents are not caused by the earth spinning at 1,038 mph.

Ocean Currents Revealed

> ."..and the fish of the sea, all that swim the paths of the seas."
> *Psalm 8:8*

Matthew Maury (1806-1873) is considered the father of oceanography. The Bible gives a knowledge of ocean currents at a time when almost nothing was known about the ocean. It was not until 1845 that Matthew Fontaine Maury, inspired by Psalm 8:8, began discovering and mapping the existence of ocean currents. Even today oceanography is hailed as the "last great frontier" of scientific study because so little is known about our oceans. His book on oceanography remains a basic source on the subject and is still used in colleges and universities.

Some people may dismiss this passage as an accidental reference, merely transposing a land-based concept (paths) to the surface of the water. But a closer look suggests that this verse distinctly refers to paths (currents) within the depths of the ocean, not upon its surface, as most fish do not swim on the surface.

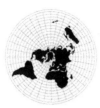

ATMOSPHERE

Today, the atmosphere is a thin blanket of gas that surrounds the earth. Ninety-nine percent of our air is within 25 miles of earth's surface. The atmosphere is divided into several layers. The lower layer, called the troposphere, is about the first six miles above earth. This is the region where most of our weather today occurs including winds, clouds, and rain. It is also the space for most airplane traffic. The stratosphere extends about six to 30 miles high. This name describes flatness, because the air in this region is visibly layered. The air in this region is not curved. The air in this region is flat above a flat earth. The stratosphere region is home to the ozone layer. Above the stratosphere are the mesophere and ionosphere. The northern lights, or aurora, occur in these upper layers, 60 to 100 miles high.

The Apostle Paul refers to the atmosphere in 2 Corinthians 12:2. He describes a man being "caught up" to the third heaven. In Genesis 1:1, God created three heavens.

Atmospheric Pressure

The Bible denies any motion of the earth. Ecclesiastes 1:4 says, "The earth abides (Hebrew: amad = stands, rests) forever." The earth stands fast in our atmosphere. We have proof for an immense height of air. Scientists tell us that the atmosphere (aeriform fluid) surrounding the earth is about fifty miles high.

Copernicans tell us that the wind at the equator surpasses speeds of more than ten times the velocity of the most fearful hurricane. Add to this a motion of the earth around the sun and another of the sun through space, and you have astounding speed of 50 miles in a second. Would not the air be entirely lost? Or, at least follow the earth like the tail of a comet?

Copernicans tell us the air is pressed tight to the earth. Where does the air pressure begin or take place? Why can't we feel or notice something of a pressure that enormous? There's nothing of the sort to feel in the least. We can see smoke rise freely and undisturbed up in the air, as the clouds calmly float to and fro over us. Airplanes rise and ascend above the clouds, but nowhere is the swift motion of the earth or heavy air pressure felt.

The Course of Trade Winds

The opponents to biblical truth see that the great pressure is caused by the earth's rotation. They have always contended that the Trade Winds in the hot belt are caused by the swiftly moving earth.

Ecclesiastes 1:6 informs us, "The wind blows to the south and turns to the north; round and round it goes, ever returning on its course."

This was a remarkable statement given the earth's primitive knowledge of atmospheric conditions. In Solomon's time (Ecclesiastes was written around 935 BC) there were no scientific revelations about the trade winds that move in a regular, predictable pattern around the earth. Sailors finally began mapping these winds during the age of exploration about 2,000 years after this was written.

Ocean Floor

There are springs that arise from the ocean floor according to Job 38:16. Mountains and deep valleys exist on the ocean floor according to Job 38:16 and Jonah 2:5-6.

Four Winds

- Jeremiah 49:36 - 4 winds
- Daniel 7:2 - 4 winds
- Matthew 24:31 - 4 winds
- Revelation 7:1 - 4 winds

Jet Stream

There is a jet stream that connects North America with Europe. Commercial aircraft fly in the jet stream to conserve fuel. The jet stream is 1,000 to 3,000 long. It is one to three miles thick. Jet streams are located five to nine miles above Earth's surface in the mid to upper troposphere. There are four jet streams, two in the north and two in the southern hemisphere. The winds blow from west to east in the jet streams. Often the winds shift to the north and south. There are three-cell circulations: 1) Polar air; 2) Temperate air; and 3) Tropical air. A jet stream affects weather. The fast moving air currents in a jet stream can transport weather systems across the United States, affecting temperature and precipitation.

How did the authors who penned the Bible know about the jet streams? God revealed it to them. The jet streams were only discovered in the 1920s when aircraft could fly that high to discover them.

Cross Ventilation

Cross ventilation is a natural method of cooling. The system allows wind to force cool exterior air into a building through an inlet or vent while an outlet forces warm interior air outside through an outlet or vent. It takes two vents for cross ventilation to work.

The Earth has a cross ventilation system to cool the Earth's atmosphere. A cross ventilation system would not work on a ball earth. Something has to feed the air into the system. How can you control the air system on a ball earth spinning at 1,038 mph?

We have a dome shaped earth that requires cross ventilation. The four angels control the four winds of the earth. Each of them control the four jet streams like a leaf blower. They feed the jet stream into the system by an inlet. See: Jeremiah 49:36.

Revelation 7:1 says:

"After this I saw four angels standing at the four corners of the earth, holding back the four winds of the earth, that no wind might blow on earth or sea or against any tree."

NUMERICAL LANGUAGES

Psalm 147:5 says: "...his understanding is beyond measure or infinite..."

Both Hebrew and Greek are numerical languages. Each letter is assigned a specific number. Neither the early Hebrews or Greeks used Arabic numerals to represent numbers. They used a letter corresponding to the number. Hebrew has 22 consonants. No vowels. The vowels are added. Aleph = 1. Beth = 2, etc.

Genesis 1:1 is composed of seven Hebrew words containing a total of 28 letters. Throughout the Bible the number seven appears repeatedly as a symbol of divine perfection - the seven days of creation, God rested on the seventh day, the seven churches, the seven seals, the seven trumpets, etc. You have seven holes in your head: two ears, two eyes, two nostrils, one mouth = 7.

The number 3.1416 is the value of the number of the Hebrew letters in Genesis 1:1. Each letter of the Hebrew alphabet has a numeric value. The number of letters x the product of the letters. The number of words x the product of the words. You get the value of pi to four decimal places. The ratio is the same for all circles and is approximately 3.1416.

The Bible is describing a circle, not a sphere. Only a flat geo stationary circular earth fits that description. The Bible is describing the creation of the earth in words with numerical value. The secret meaning behind those words is a mathematical formula that verifies the authenticity of the text and describes the shape of the earth - circular.

"For nothing is hidden that will not be made manifest, nor is
anything secret that will not be known and come to light."
Luke 8:17 ESV

Worldwide Catastrophic Event

The cause of the geological formation is recorded in Genesis 7. Here is the record
of a worldwide catastrophic event that totally changed the face of the flat Earth.
God gave the green Earth a face lift. It has never looked the same since.

Water—The Ultimate Cure

Pure water is, next to oxygen, the most fundamental element necessary for life.
This simple compound of three atoms makes up 67% of our body weight. A 2%
decrease results in fatigue. A 10% drop causes significant problems and greater
losses can be fatal. Good hydration cushions bones and joints, transports nutri-
ents, flushes toxins, regulates body temperature, and empowers the body's natural
processes of healing. Water is the ultimate cure. Drink eight glasses of pure water
daily. Add fresh lemon.

Pre-Flood Weather Report

Brought to you by the Noah and Sons Construction Company. Welcome to our
tropical Paradise. Ideal temperature. Pleasant greenhouse effect. Rich soil. Abundance of nutritional food. Tropical lush vegetation. Large forests. Fertile land
mass. Plenty of pure water. Invisible canopy cover. Solar energy through greenhouse windows, but no ozone. No clouds. No rain. No severe storms. No deserts.
No cold polar regions. No frozen wastelands. No strong winds. Long periods of
twilight. Heavy dew. No violent animals.

Adam and Eve were originally unclothed yet comfortable because the climate
was tropical. Perfect temperature.

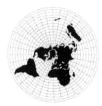

THE CANOPY THEORY

A layer of invisible water vapor surrounded the earth from the time of creation until the Genesis Flood.

We begin with examining several verses in Scripture that introduce us to the concept of a different world prior to the Flood.

And God said, "Let there be an expanse between the waters to separate water from water." So God made an expanse and separated the water under the expanse from the water above it. And it was so. God called the expanse "sky." And there was evening, and there was morning - the second day."

Genesis 1:6-8 NIV

An expanse, or firmament, divided a layer of water which was above from a layer of water below. What are the "waters above?" A thick blanket of moisture surrounding the Earth in the form of a canopy. After God created light (Genesis 1:3), He made a distinction between the waters on the Earth and the water above the Earth by raising the land (continents) and forcing the oceans into their appointed place. Genesis 2:6 is the first evidence of a vapor canopy.

God did not create on Day Two. He rearranged what He had already made. The second day is the only day God did not pronounce it good because He did not bring anything new into existence.

The first irrigation system was a mist that went up from the Earth and watered the surface of the ground. Genesis 2:5-6 uses the phrase "but streams came up from the Earth and watered the whole surface of the ground." Streams can also refer to rising water vapor.

In the pre-Flood world, there was no rain (Genesis 2:5). The ground was watered by a daily mist, or dew. There was a system of rivers fed by artesian springs coming from the "great deep," an immense system of underground pressurized reservoirs.

The canopy was a covering of water molecules in the form of ice crystals. Mathematical calculations estimate the base of the pre-Flood canopy at 20 to 25 miles above the Earth. The thickness of the canopy was around five to six miles.

The Hebrew word mabbul has been translated in English as "flood" in Genesis 6 and 7. This word is found 13 times in the OT, and is commonly translated as "flood." It also has the meaning of "over abundance" or "destruction from above." A better translation would be "the canopy."

The Flood caused the death of all men and beasts on Earth. It also caused destruction in the heavens. The "water above" (canopy - mabbul) - or the heavenly ocean - broke forth upon the Earth below and caused a catastrophe both in the heavens and on the Earth.

The water vapor canopy acted as a shield much like a sponge - absorbing and deflecting harmful radiation coming from outer space. With the water vapor canopy and the ozone canopy, radiation coming toward Earth would be absorbed or deflected to protect life on the Earth.

Ozone (0_3) is a gas formed and concentrated primarily in the upper atmosphere. The ozone layer is about the thickness of a pane of window glass. A blanket of triatomic oxygen is called ozone (0_3). "Out in the ozone" is 20 miles above the surface of the Earth. The ozone layer acts as a protective shield, as the vapor canopy did in the pre-Flood world. Post-Flood ozone levels are less than the pre-Flood levels. Oxygen (0_2) is a health-producing gas. Ozone (03) is a health destroying gas.

The great Flood caused the canopy to collapse. This is where the 40 days and 40 nights of non-stop torrential rain came from.

After the great Flood, God devised a new system for watering the Earth. He activated the hydrologic cycle. This is a slow and continuous dripping or mist which allows maximum water absorption. The post-Flood watering system is a water-vapor cycle (evaporation, condensation, precipitation, and transpiration).

Prior to the Flood, the fertility of the soil was superior in composition, enriched with minerals and elements and all things necessary for producing bountiful and healthy harvests. The entire flat earth was covered with rich soil. Fruit trees, nut trees, and vegetation all grew to enormous sizes. The flood washed most of the top soil and its enriched minerals into the oceans. Most of the earth is non-productive due to lack of water, overuse of soil and contamination. Restoration of land requires rest and fertilization.

Fiber optics are strains of transparent glass fibers, strains of glass smaller than a human hair. They demonstrate the effects of filtered sunlight. Fiber optics allow sunlight to pass through strains of tubular glass while filtering out lethal ultraviolet rays. This is an illustration of the original environment under the canopy. The canopy allowed disused life-giving light to penetrate while filtering out harmful radiation.

Prior to the Flood, the vapor canopy produced a greenhouse effect. What is the greenhouse effect? Air trapped inside a greenhouse is warmer than air outside. Sun rays (shortwave radiation-A) pass through the glass of a greenhouse and are absorbed by the plants inside. The plants release heat back into the air (long wave radiation-B). The heat is trapped, and the temperature rises. The temperature and humidity can be maintained year round.

It is possible that much of the water in the oceans today was stored in a great vapor canopy across the flat Earth. The oceans were smaller before the Flood.

The water vapor provided uniform temperature worldwide. The result was lush vegetation. The testimony of the rocks reveal abundant vegetation. Fossils show that the Earth was covered with lush vegetation.

Prior to the flood of Noah, the average year-round temperature never dropped below freezing. There were tropical forests with 90-foot fruit trees all over the flat earth. Some places are now frigid zones or dry deserts. In the past, there were no summer months nor winter months as we have today. There was a semi-tropical climate with mild temperatures and a good growing season all year long.

Prior to the Flood, everything was giant size. Giant lizards, we now call dinosaurs, weighing over 40 tons. Full-grown dinosaurs devoured hundreds of pounds of vegetation daily. Fossils show mammals were 30-40% greater in length and height. Crocodiles grew to 50 feet in length. Reptilian like-birds had wingspans of over 50 feet from wing tip to wing tip. Insects were an enormous size. Fossilized cockroaches over a foot in length have been found.

The fossil record reveals that all creatures once grew to be much larger than those today. The evidence in the rocks shows humans were much larger in the past. A 25-inch footprint has been discovered in rock formations. Adam could have been 16 feet tall. Noah 15 feet tall. King Og 14+ feet tall. Goliath 9+ feet tall. Modern man 6 feet tall. The Israelite spies said they felt like grasshoppers compared to the giants they saw in the Promised Land (Numbers 13:31-33).

Prior to the Flood, man lived longer. The Bible teaches that the early patriarchs often lived to be nearly 1,000 years old and had children when they were several hundred years old. According to the Bible, God created Adam and Eve without sin and with the ability to live forever. For 1,500 years after the creation, men lived longer lives. The ten patriarchs (excluding Enoch) who preceded the Great Flood lived an average of 912 years. Adam lived 930 years. Seth 912 years. Enosh 905 years. Calnan 910 years. Mahalalel 895 years. Jared 962 years. Enoch 365 years (translated). Methuselah 969 years. Lamech 777 years. Noah 950 Years.

After Noah's Flood, man's life span began to decline (Genesis 11), and all life forms began to decrease in size.

Air has weight but it is invisible to the human eye. Air can be measured accurately. The weight of air creates atmospheric pressure. The weather report calls it barometric pressure. A change in the barometric reading indicates a change in the weight of air. It has been calculated that the pre-Flood atmospheric pressure was about 2-1/4 times greater than that of today. This increased the ability of the pterodactyl (big bird) to fly. Pilots have learned that it is easier to take off at lower altitudes where the air pressure is greater.

Giant dinosaurs weighing over 50 tons survived prior to the Flood because there was 100% oxygen level and high atmospheric pressure. With weightier atmospheric pressure, a greater amount of oxygen was available to the biomass (skin & tissue) of the giant creatures - allowing them to live longer, healthier lives and grow larger. These gigantic creatures received enough oxygen for their huge tissue mass. A 100-ton supersaurus had a small lung capacity. It could never get enough oxygen to circulate through its entire body to survive with today's lower air pressure.

In the post-Flood environment many dinosaurs were unable to survive in a climate with reduced atmospheric pressure. They suffocated or became disabled. They were easy prey for other meat-eating creatures.

Human life is not evolving into larger, stronger, and better people. Many of the life forms found in rocks are basically the same. A fossilized fish is a fish. There are no half-fish and half-birds found in the fossil records. Job 8:8-10 reveals that modern man, in terms of intelligence, is but a shadow of ancient man. Man's intelligence and achievements have been deteriorating because of sin. Human beings are not evolving into a higher level of intelligence.

Prior to the Flood of Noah, weather conditions were very stable. Did it rain before the Flood? Genesis 2:5-6 states that ""Elohim had not caused it to rain on the land." No rain. It continues, "a mist was going up from the land and was watering the whole face (flat surface) of the ground." The whole earth was watered by the heavy mist. This was the only water source after Adam was created by Elohim. Some argue that this passage describes the environment before Adam was created. They are speculating about the pre-Flood environment. Nowhere does the Genesis account of creation state that Elohim (the Creator in Genesis 1:1) stopped the mist as a watering source and replaced it with rain clouds and rain. The first time the Bible records falling rain is in Genesis 7:1-4. God told Noah that rain was going to destroy every living thing on the earth. It was a worldwide flat earth flood (Genesis 6:17; 7:19-20, 22). God caused the first rain in the 600th year of Noah's life. The rain fell upon the earth for 40 days and 40 nights (Genesis 7:11-12). Non-stop torrential rain. It was a record setting downpour. My, my, didn't it rain!

Man did not eat meat before the Flood. Genesis 1:29-30 gives only seed-bearing vegetation for man's diet. But after the Flood, God issued a new dietary plan that included meat. Leviticus identifies the animals to be eaten. God gave a post-Flood command to eat meat in Genesis 9:3. "Everything that lives and moves will be food for you." Grass-fed meat is one of the best sources of magnesium, which is related to calcium. It builds strong bones.

Plants are chemical factories that pick up carbon dioxide, a waste product that both man and animals exhale. Plants convert carbon dioxide into oxygen, which both man and animals require for survival. God designed the exchange of gases between plant life and animal kingdoms for the express purpose of making the Earth hospitable for life.

Blessed are the balanced. CO_2 is the gas that plant life thrives on, and human life thrives on the oxygen they produce. God designed two kingdoms: one for the plants and one for beasts, birds, insects, fish and man. There is balance and harmony in nature. Both provide for the other. Now isn't that cool?

Prior to the Flood the CO_2 level was about 15 times greater than today. More CO_2 level in the air means more growth of all plants. The greater the growth and size of plant life means more oxygen for birds, animals and humans. More oxygen for animals and humans means healthier bodies and increased mental capabilities. Now isn't that neat! A reduction in the amount of oxygen to brain cells is considered a major cause of aging and the diseases associated with aging.

Increased levels of humidity (H_2O) and carbon dioxide (CO_2) slow the aging and maturing process.

God designed the oceans to absorb CO_2 from the atmosphere. The cooler the temperature of the oceans, the greater their absorption rate. There was a reduction of CO_2 in the atmosphere after the Flood. The oceans became colder. The more frigid the ocean temperature, the less CO_2 will remain in the atmosphere. Cold oceans absorb CO_2 right out of the atmosphere, like a sponge. Before the Flood, the average water temperature of the oceans was 60°.F. Today, the average ocean water temperature is 38°F. God set in motion new laws and cycles to maintain life after the Flood.

God provides the sunshine and the rain. Matthew 5:45 tells us that God causes His sun to rise on the evil and the good, and sends rain on the righteous and the unrighteous. With the Psalmist, we praise God for the blessing of rain (Psalm 147:7-8). The Hebrew word for rain in Genesis 8:2 is gesem, which means water drops.

Hebrews 11:7 tells us that "by faith Noah, being warned of God of things not seen as yet, moved with fear, prepared an ark." What does the "things not seen" refer to? Rain or the Flood or both? No one had seen rain before Noah's Flood. However, the Flood was no surprise to Noah. Enoch's secret word was Methuselah in Genesis 5:21-25. God gave a special prophetic vision to Enoch. Methuselah was Enoch's son. He lived 969 years. The oldest man in the Bible. The year of Methuselah's death was in 1656 BC. A great judgment would be sent upon the world when he died. Enoch had been warning about the flood for 300 years before it happened.

The first water drops came from the water canopy. The water drops fell for 40 days and 40 nights. Verse 19 tells us that the surface of the water was 15 cubits (22.5 feet or 6.858 miles) higher than the highest mountain. No mountain played peekaboo during the flooding. There were all hidden. Once again, the whole earth was completely covered with water, like in Genesis 1:2. God started over after the Flood. He gave Noah and his sons the same Cultural Mandate that He had given to Adam and Eve in Genesis 1:28.

What the hail? In Exodus 9:18, 23 we are told that God would send a very heavy hail on the land of Egypt. Never before seen in Egypt from the day it was founded. God created the boundaries of the nations (Acts 17:26). Hail is frozen water drops. Rain with cold air causes rain drops to freeze.

God produced the Flood which caused great changes in the surface of the earth. The fountains of the deep were broken up. There was volcanic activity, disruption of the tectonic plates, a configuration of land masses, and a deepening of the oceans to hold the floodwaters. This resulted in permanent changes in the topography and climate. The climate and atmosphere on earth was semi-tropical prior to the Flood. There were no cold-core weather systems, no fluffy white clouds, no rain clouds, no dark cloud rain storms, no snow storms, and no cold front or high winds. There were no hurricanes or tornadoes. Every night, the stars were visible as they twinkled the glory of God to man. God's craftsmanship was on display. It was paradise on earth. There was 100% air pressure and 100% oxygen, like in a hyperbaric oxygen chamber. All living creatures lived longer and grew larger, including man. The Flood was catastrophic to the earth. It changed everything on earth, including weather patterns. It caused the original climate change.

Many ancient cultures have traditions telling of a canopy-type phenomenon above the earth. The Babylonian creation account, Enum Elish, refers to Munmu, representing fog, clouds, or mist.

The Rainbow

Rainbows hold a fascination for mankind. We read about a rainbow encircling the throne of the King of the Universe - Christ Jesus. There is a 360° full circle bow around God's throne in the 3rd heaven (Revelation 4:3). Rainbows were not in existence under the pre-Flood canopy (Genesis 9:12-16). God sets a rainbow in the clouds when the rain is ending. God calls the rainbow "my bow in the cloud." God owns it. Seven colors. ROYGBIC - aka the rainbow. It was a sign of the covenant between God and the earth. It has a special significance as a token of God's promise to never again send a worldwide Flood on the flat earth.

What causes a rainbow? It is the result of bending light rays through water droplets. The curving causes the color bands of light to separate so that various colors of white light become visible. When all the shades of light are mixed, they produce the "color" white. You can bend light, but you cannot bend water. An observer sees a rainbow when he is at an angle of about 42° from the path of the sun's direct rays. Rainbows without rain can be produced by a spray or mist, such as by a water fall or hot spring geyser or garden hose. These are natural occurrences of rainbows.

Ebb and Flow of Tides

There is a constant pressure of the atmosphere on the surface of the Earth and the Oceans. This is shown by ordinary barometrical observations and many gas experiments. The mass of the Moon is less than the mass of Earth. The mass of the Moon is not great enough to affect the tides in the Oceans on Earth. The cause of the tides in the Oceans should be looked for in some other reason. The mutual attraction between the Earth and the Moon should be given up. That the Moon causes the tides to ebb and flow is another lie of Darwinian evolution.

During the most fearsome storms at sea only the surface is turbulent. The ocean water is always calm at the depth of about one hundred feet of water, except in the path of well-marked currents in the sea. Most terrible tempests are superficial. Calm water is found at the depth of 90 feet during the greatest storms. At the depth of 90 feet the sea is perfectly calm.

What is the general cause of tides? There is a continual pressure of the atmosphere upon the Earth. The Earth is a vast plane "stretched out upon the waters" (Psalm 136:6). The water level, out of necessity, slightly fluctuates. The water level slowly rises and falls in the water. From the movement of the atmosphere, the Earth is slowly depressed, and the water moves towards the receding shoreline and produces the flood tide. From the reaction of the resisting oceanic average the Earth gradually goes up the waters retreat, and the ebb tide is produced. A raft or a ship have a gentle floating motion on the water. This gradual rising and falling of the floating mass is always more or less observable even in calm water and a calm atmosphere. Vessels of different sizes fluctuate with different velocities. Large and heavy vessels move the least rapidly. The Earth, which is proportionately larger than a ship, makes a fluctuation once only in about twelve hours.

The action or pressure upon earth's atmosphere, and the reaction or resistance of the water to it, may be traced to all the main distinctive features of the tides.

The Earth has a vibrating or quavering motion, which is true of a floating and fluctuating vessel. This has been the experience of astronomers and surveyors.

A Spirit Level is a tool used to indicate how parallel (level) or perpendicular (plumb) a surface is relative to the earth. A spirit level gets its name from the mineral spirit solution inside the level to create an air-bubble.

If a sensitive spirit-level is placed on a rock or a solid foundation, the peculiar physical process can be observed to have constant change in the position of the air-bubble. No matter how carefully the level may be adjusted, and the instrument protected from the atmosphere, the bubble will move from its position many times in seconds because the Earth is vibrating. Instruments of the best construction cannot always be relied upon without occasional readjustment.

Hot Springs

The deeper we descend into the interior of the Earth, the higher the temperature rises. Terrestrial heat increases with increasing depth. The temperature of the Earth at a depth of 50 feet (from sea level) is the same in winter and in summer.

Within the depth of Earth it is very hot. Where springs of water are found at deep levels, the mineral water is used for baths and medicine for the sick. The deepest Artesian wells are the warmest. Spring water brought to the surface is warm mineral water.

At a depth of one and a half miles, all water is boiling. At a depth of about ten miles all rocks are melted. The surface of the Earth is covered with a solid crust, ranging from three to 43.5 miles in depth. It is the outermost layer. The crust is thickest under high mountains and thinnest beneath the ocean. The Earth's core is the same temperature as the surface of the sun. At the center of the Earth, within a liquid outer core, is an orb of solid iron. Whenever Earth's crust breaks open, there is a gush of lava, fire, melted rocks, fiery gasses, and ashes.

Mount St. Helens

Mount St. Helens is an active stratovolcano located in Washington State in the Pacific Northwest. On May 18, 1980, a cataclysmic eruption took place, the deadliest and most economically destructive volcanic event in U.S. history. The massive debris avalanche erupted after pressure from a magnitude 5.1 earthquake. 57 people were killed; 200 homes, 47 bridges, 15 miles of railways, and 185 miles of highway were destroyed. The eruption caused terrestrial ecosystems near the volcano to decrease biological production. Aquatic ecosystems in the area benefited from the amounts of ash, which allowed life to multiply rapidly. Six years after the eruption, most lakes in the area went back to their normal level because water seeks it own level

Now Mount St. Helens is a popular tourist attraction. It has become a favorite hiking location and it is climbed year round.

Mount St. Helens changed the future of volcanology.

THE DAYS OF NOAH AND THE NEPHILIM

So what did Jesus mean when He said, "As it was in the days of Noah" (Matthew 24:37)? What was it like in the days of Noah? What is the reality? Principle: don't condemn before investigation.

Genesis 6:1-8 is the account of increasing corruption and wickedness on earth, which is the given reason for the Flood of Noah. What happened in these verses is bizarre and very strange. There are three views of who the Nephilim were is Verse 4. The three views are:

1. The Tyrant View (no biblical support)
2. The Line of Seth View (no biblical support)
3. The Angel View (biblical and historical support)

"Line of Seth" View

The Line of Seth View is taught in most seminaries today. This view is contrived. There is no biblical support for this view. Seminary students are being taught the wrong interpretation of who the offspring were called Nephilim.

The Angel View

The Angel View is the biblical view. It was the traditional view that was taught until the 5th century AD. The following is the Angel View.

Jesus' Confidential Briefing

Four disciples (Peter, James, John and Andrew) ask Jesus about His Return

Jesus gives details in three Gospels, known as the Olivet Discourse.

- Matthew 24, 25
- Mark 13
- Luke 21, 22

Jesus Personal Warning

Opening statement:

> "Watch out that no one deceives you"
> *Matthew 24:4 ESV*

In spiritual matters, the enemy will attempt to deceive us.

Jesus' Strange Warning

> "For as it was in the days of Noah,
> so will be the coming of the Son of Man"
> *Matthew 24:37 ESV*

What does that mean? What were the days of Noah like?

Genesis 6:1-2 is One Sentence

> "When man began to multiply on the face of the land
> and daughters were born to them, the sons of God saw
> that the daughters of man were attractive,
> and they took as their wives any they chose."

"Sons of God" in Hebrew: Bene HaElohim = angels. This is a term used of a direct creation of God. Adam was a direct creation of God. Human beings are not. We are sons of Adam, but, according to John 1:12 and Romans 8:14-15, we can become sons of God.

Angels

Job 1:6, 2:1, 38:7 Bene HaElohim is used of angels in these verses, a direct creation of God.

Luke 20:36 refers to angels.

The Book of Enoch also refers to angels. The Book of Enoch is not an inspired book, but it is useful in understanding the vocabulary and grammar of the time.

Septuagint (LXX) makes it clear we are dealing with angels. The Septuagint was the product of 70 top scholars who took about 15 years to complete the translation. Started about 385 BC and finished about 270 BC. The Hebrew Bible, the Tanakh, was translated from Hebrew to Greek, which gives us the benefit of the precision of the Greek language.

Greek was the common language spoken and written during the Hellenistic period and the Roman Empire. It was the enforced language in commerce, thanks to Alexander the Great. The Jews had to speak Greek in order to survive in business. They knew Hebrew for religious purposes. The NT was written in Koine Greek, also known as Alexandrian dialect. Koine means common.

- Bene HaElohim = "Sons of God," a term for angels.
- Benoth Adam = "Daughters of Adam," Adam's daughters.
- Nephilim - mighty men which were of old; men of renown.

Verse 4 - The Nephilim were the offspring of a strange and unnatural union. The Sons of God were fallen angels. A fallen angel is a demon. Demons are wicked. The passage portrays fallen angels, or demons.

Shocking as it seems, evidently, men on earth invited fallen angels, demons, to indwell them. A demon will not enter a human unless they are given permission to do so. These demons possessed men had sex with the daughters of Adam. The offspring were called the Nephilim. They came in to the daughters of men, the daughters of Adam, and bore children to them, called the Nephilim, which became mighty men; giant in physical stature and extraordinarily strong. The children of this most strange union were the Nephilim. The offspring were all male, no females. The phrase and they took as their wives any they chose, indicates the sexual union was forced.

The Nephilim

- Nephilim—"the fallen ones"
- Nephal (verb)—"to fall, be cast down, to fall away, desert"
- HaGibborim—offspring—"the mighty ones"
- gigantes—"giants"
- gigas—"earth born;" the root word for gene

This passage portrays fallen angels, who were not the good angels
Septuagint (Greek) LXX brought confusion because it used the word gigante—"giants"—it sounds like giants, but that's not what the word means, although they were giants. Extremely large in physical stature, with six fingers.
The Nature of Angels
They always appear in human form
At Sodom and Gomorrah; the homosexuals lusted after the angels. The angels were male.
At the Resurrection of Jesus a pair of angels
At the Ascension of Jesus a pair of angels
They spoke, took men by the hand, and ate meals
Capable of Direct Physical Combat
At the Passover in Egypt
The angel killed 185,000 Syrian soldiers (2 Kings 19:35)
Human beings and angels don't marry in heaven

Can Angels Have Sex?

> "For in the resurrection they neither marry, nor are given in marriage, but are as the angels of God in heaven."
> *Matthew 22:30; Mark 12:25*

This verse is referring to believers in heaven. They are immortal and don't have sex. Mortal beings on earth procreate. Immortal beings in heaven do not procreate. He's talking about the good angels in heaven who behave.

Sexual union in marriage on earth is a physical illustration of a spiritual reality in heaven. Believers are one in Christ.

"Habitation"

Strong's Concordance Greek: 3613 oiketerion

Usage: a dwelling-place, habitation, abode; referring to the body as a dwelling place for the spirit.

Only occurs twice in the Bible.

1. Jude 6 - habitation from which the angels had "disrobed." These angels took off their robes of righteousness to practice immorality.

2. 2 Corinthians 5:2 - alluding to the heavenly body with which the believer longs to be "clothed." Believers will be clothed in robes of righteousness in our eternal house in heaven. We will not be found naked. Adam and Eve lost their robes of righteousness when they sinned. Suddenly, they were found naked.

Demons Always Seek Embodiment

They can posses a human being.

The demons in Matthew 8 occupied the bodies of two men in the Gadarenes. Jesus restored the demon-possessed man.

Demons are hostile. They need permission to enter a person. In Matthew 8, the demons begged Jesus repeatedly to let them go into pigs, and he gave them permission. They did not want to go to the abyss. The demons came out of the man and entered a large herd of pigs (Luke 8:26-35).

Why pigs? The large herd of pigs was owned by some Jewish businessmen. Jews were not supposed to have anything to do with pigs. Pigs are not kosher.

The Unnatural Offspring

Nephilim, the offspring of an ungodly union

Supernatural offspring: "Mighty men"

All male offspring

No "women of renown"

What made Noah's genealogy so distinctive? Genesis 6:9

The Generation of Noah

Genesis 6:9 says Noah was a just man and perfect in his generations. Noah walked with God. What does perfect mean?

tamiym = "without blemish, sound, healthful, without spot, unimpaired." Noah's genealogy was unblemished. His family was not part of the Nephilim. Post-flood Nephilim

God instructed Joshua to wipe out these tribes because they were descendants of the Nephilim. No compromise. Wipe out every man, woman, and child because there was a gene pool problem Why? Because Satan was using these tribes to keep Israel from possessing its land.

Arba, Anak and his seven sons (Anakim), encountered them while exploring Canaan. Bad report of the land from 10 spies: "We saw the Nephilim there" (the descendants of Anak come from the Nephilim). We seemed like grasshoppers in our own eyes, and we looked the same to them." (Numbers 13:33 NIV). The Hebrew word Nephilim is used here.

Og, King of Bashan (Deuteronomy 3:11; Joshua 12). Bashan was known as the "king of the giants."

These hybrids were between 10 and 13 feet tall. Tall and powerful offspring. The offspring were unusually tall, strong and powerful. For some reason, Pastor John MacArthur teaches that there was no difference between the Nephilum and the offspring born before the unnatural unions with fallen angels. If there was no difference, than why did God destroy them? Sure there was a difference. The Nephilum were called "Mighty Men" for a reason. Because they were taller, bigger, and stronger than the previous offspring. Everyone was afraid of them. They were like Superman with evil intentions. The 10 spies in Canaan reported that they looked like grasshoppers to the Nephilum (Numbers 13:33 NIV). This supernatural offspring was violent, wicked, destructive, immoral and every intention of the thoughts of their heart was only evil continually. They were guilty of crimes against humanity. This is precisely why God drowned them all in deep water and destroyed the whole flat and fixed earth in the Great Deluge 1,656 years after the creation.

Goliath and his four brothers were descendants of Anak. (2 Samuel 21:16-22; 1 Chronicles 20:4-8).

Angel View

The correct view is the Angel View. If this view is correct, it will be confirmed in the NT.

Three NT Confirmations

1. Jude 6,7 (The Book of Jude has only one chapter)
2. 1 Peter 3:19-20
3. 2 Peter 2:4-5

(1)

> "And the angels who did not stay within their own position
> of authority, but left their proper dwelling, he has kept
> in eternal chains under gloomy darkness until the judgment
> of the great day—just as Sodom and Gomorrah
> and the surrounding cities, which likewise indulged
> in sexual immorality and pursued unnatural desire, serve
> as an example by undergoing a punishment of eternal fire."
> *Jude 6, 7 ESV*

Jude is talking about judgment on the wicked, and he mentions these angels who did not keep their proper domain, but left their own abode back in Genesis 6. These angels that participated in sexual immorality are chained awaiting a special judgment. Jude makes a comparison between the sins of Sodom and Gomorrah and the sins of these disrobed angels, in that they were doing that which is unnatural. The angels went after strange flesh, so did the homosexuals in Sodom and Gomorrah.

(3)

> *"For if God did not spare angels when they sinned, but cast them*
> *into hell (Greek: Tartarus) and committed them to chains of gloomy*
> *darkness to be kept until the judgment; if he did not spare the ancient*

world, but preserved Noah, a herald of righteousness, with seven
others, when he brought a flood upon the world of the ungodly."

2 Peter 2:4-5 ESV

Peter links the bad angels to the days of Noah.

Tartarus

Atlas and Hercules from Greek mythology were what would be called in the Hebrew, Nephilim, offspring of an intermarriage between a god and a woman. A hybrid of this unnatural union that produced giants with supernatural strength.

Goliath and his four brothers were descendants of Nephilim (2 Samuel 21:16-22; 1 Chronicles 20:4-8). Goliath of Gath, whose height was six cubits and a span (over nine and a half feet tall), was hired by the Philistines to challenge Israel and Israel's God. David, a shepherd lad, chose five smooth stones from the brook and put them in his shepherd's porch. His sling was in his hand and he approached the Philistine. David said, "I come to you in the name of the LORD of hosts." He took out one stone from his bag and slung it and struck the Philistine on his forehead. The stone sank into his forehead, and he fell on his face to the ground. David took Goliath's sword and cut off his head with it. David defeated Goliath (1 Samuel 17). The battle is the LORD'S.

(2)

"In which he went and proclaimed to the spirits in prison,
because they formerly did not obey, when God's patience waited
in the days of Noah, while the ark was being prepared, in which a
few, that is, eight persons, were brought safely through water."
1 Peter 3:21-22

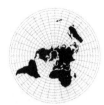

THE ORIGINAL WARFARE

"I will put enmity between you and the woman
and between your offspring (seed) and her offspring (seed);
he shall bruise your head, and you shall bruise his heel."
Genesis 3:15 ESV

God declared war on Satan.

Messianic title - "seed of the woman."

Women don't have seed. This refers to the Virgin Birth by the Holy Spirit.

Our Warfare

In Ephesians 6:12, Paul gives a list of fallen angels in their hierarchical order. These are real fallen angels, not to be played with.

For we wrestle not against flesh and blood, but

- against principalities
- against powers
- against the rulers of the darkness of this world
- against spiritual wickedness in high places

Summary - The wickedness of the people made God regret that He had created man and made Him resolve to send a flood that would destroy all the living creatures on the flat earth.

The Text Tells Us Why God Sent the Worldwide Catastrophic Flood of Noah

"The LORD saw that the wickedness of man was great in the
earth, and that every intention of the thoughts of his heart was
only evil continually. And the LORD was sorry that he had made
man on the earth, and it grieved him to his heart."
Genesis 6:5-6 ESV

"Now the earth was corrupt in God's sight and the earth
was filled with violence. And God saw the earth, and behold,
it was corrupt, for all flesh had corrupted their way
on the earth. I have determined to make an end of all flesh,
for the earth is filled with violence through them."
Genesis 6:11-13 ESV

Noah's Flood—A Worldwide Catastrophe

Enoch "walked with God: and he was no more; for God took him" (Genesis 5:21-24). Enoch lived 365 years before he was taken by God. He entered heaven alive before dying. Methuselah was the son of Enoch, the father of Lamech, and the grandfather of Noah. Methuselah was the oldest person in human history, dying at the age of 969 (Genesis 5:27). At age 65, God revealed to Enoch the reality of the coming Flood. Enoch spent three centuries warning of God's impending judgment (Jude 14-15). The Flood came as no surprise because Enoch spent three hundred years warning the wicked people of coming judgment. Methuselah's name is translated "man of the javelin." God promised that Divine wrath would not fall until after Methuselah died. The fact that Methuselah lived such a long life is a symbol of God's mercy. This demonstrated the longsuffering nature of God. Raindrops started to fall the year Methuselah died.

Genesis 1-11 is literal history. It happened just as the text says. The cosmos and everything in it is only about 6,000 years old. Creation geologists do not accept the claim made by Darwinian evolutionists that the Earth is billions of years old. Genesis teaches that the flood was a worldwide, year-long, catastrophic event about 4,500 years ago. The time from Adam until Noah's flood was 1,656 years.

The flood of Noah was not a global event because the Earth is not a globe; it is not a round ball. The flood was worldwide because the Earth is a flat plane.

The flood of Noah produced an astounding amount of erosion and sedimentation and buried many plants and animals in those sediments, which later became fossils as the sediments hardened into rock. Creation geologists believe the flood produced exactly the kind of geological features that we see all over the earth. The walls of the Grand Canyon in Arizona are a good example. Most, if not all, of the fossil-bearing sedimentary rock layers are the result of the flood. The rock layers cannot be the result of hundreds of millions of years of erosion and sedimentation, as Darwinian evolutionists claim.

Noah's flood was real, not a myth. It did happen. It was not a localized flood in the Mesopotamian Valley of the Tigris and Euphrates Rivers (modern-day Iraq). It was a vast worldwide flood that covered the whole Earth with water.

The ark's size provided maximum stability, strength, and comfort for Noah's family of eight and every living creature on board to survive the worst storm conditions on sea. The dimensions of Noah's ark are specified in Genesis Chapter 6. The measurements of the ark in its length-width-height ratio are used in naval architecture today. Noah's ark is arguably the earliest example of applied naval architecture. Noah was the world's first navel ARKitect. It was a big boat built to float.

The Genesis flood account describes things that happened on specific days in the 600th and 601st years of Noah's life. Noah lived 350 years after the flood. Noah lived a total of 950 years, and then he died.

God saw that the wickedness of man was great on the earth, and that every intention of the thoughts of his heart was only evil continually (Genesis 6:5). The Earth was filled with violence. God also destroyed all land animals and birds not on the ark and destroyed the surface of the earth.

The flood waters covered all the high mountains under heaven by 25 feet. From the time it started to rain until the eight people and all the animals disembarked the ark on dry land was 371 days (Genesis 7:11 and 8:14). Continuous, torrential rain lasted 40 days. The fountains of the deep closed up and the rain stopped on the 150th day. It took another 211 days for the water to gradually recede and the land to become dry.

God told Noah to take the birds and land animals onto the ark that He brought to him. Eight people repopulated the earth with human beings. The birds and land animals repopulated the earth after their kind.

The ark landed in the mountains (Hebrew: plural) of Ararat (modern-day eastern Turkey). The nearby mountains could be seen 74 days after the ark docked.

God promised Noah and his family that He would never again send another flood to destroy the earth, which included the animals, the birds, all their offspring, and the Earth itself. The rainbow was a sign of God's covenant with Noah. The seven colors of a rainbow never change. They always run in the same order. ROYGBIV

God commanded Noah and his family to be fruitful and multiply. God commanded the animals and birds to repopulate the earth. This is the same Cultural Mandate God gave to Adam and Eve in the Garden of Eden (Genesis 1:28). The Garden of Eden cannot be located today because the pre-flood Earth was totally destroyed. Eve ate Adam out of house and home.

In Genesis Chapters 6 - 11, the Hebrew word mabbul is used 12 times. It also appears in Psalm 29:10. This Hebrew noun refers to Noah's flood because mabbul is preceded by the definite article 'the.' 'The' flood of Noah, not just any flood. In the NT, the Greek word katakiusmos means 'cataclysm' in English. It is used in reference to Noah's flood.

During the 40 days of non-stop rain, earthquakes on the deep ocean floor triggered volcanic eruptions, and tsunamis. With all this turbulence during the torrential worldwide rain storm, a continual downpour, and the land eroding from the high surging floodwaters, the damage and change to the topography, geography, atmosphere, oxygen level, air pressure, temperature, environment, and weather patterns was cataclysmic. Before the flood, earth's environment was a gigantic hyperbaric oxygen chamber with 100% oxygen and 100% air pressure. Everything grew bigger and lived longer - man, animals, birds, fish, insects, and plant life. Adam lived to be 930 years old. Man and dinosaurs lived together before the flood.

During the 40 days of non-stop rain, water was moving as the earth filled up with rain water like a huge bowl. Water was moving as it emptied. Moving water eroded sediments and deposited it everywhere. There was a back-and-forth motion (Genesis 8:5). There was erosion and sedimentation during the receding stage. The material and debris deposited from the flooding was reworked during the receding stage. This historic cataclysmic event produced complex geological evidence that can be observed today - billions of dead things, buried in rock layers, laid down by water, all over the earth.

The flood waters moved east to west in America. Starting on the east coast, the massive flood waters caused the Blue Ridge mountains to form and then the waters went over the top westward to form the Rocky Mountains and then continued on to erode a huge section of land and form the Grand Canyon. The flood water pushed the eroded land west and created the Pacific Ocean shelf. The continental shelf is submerged under an area of shallow water known as a sea shelf. These sea shelves were caused by the flood of Noah, not drops in sea level during glacial periods.

The thousands of feet of sedimentary rock layers containing billions of dead creatures was formed after Adam was created, not before. There was no pre-Adamic Earth or pre-Adamic man. There is no gap between Genesis 1:1 and 1:2. Adam was innocent and sinless before the fall. He lived in a beautiful paradise on a high plateau. The geological evidence was not formed over millions of years before man appeared on the earth, as evolutionists claim. God called His creation "very good" before Adam sinned. Death, disease, and extinction came as a result of man's sin.

The fossil record was formed after Adam sinned. Sin is the result of the fall of man. The wages of sin is death. The logical reason for most of the fossil record was Noah's flood about 4,500 years ago. We believe God's Word is true about Creation, the Flood of Noah, the flat-earth, the non-moving Earth, and Geocentrism. We reject the age of the earth being millions of years old.

The pre-Flood world was advanced with art and industries of that time (Genesis 4:20-24). Now that first civilization, with its accumulations of knowledge and experience, its treasures of art and literature and industries, was gone. But the Adamic race is to have a new start in Noah and his three sons with their families.

Restraints Were Now Imposed

The duration of human life was greatly cut back. The length of a generation is much shorter. The soil takes more work and gives less in return. Meat is now included in man's diet. "Fear" towards man was put upon the beasts. The death-penalty was imposed on the slaying of man by man to lower violence and the crime rate. In the middle these restraints, the faithfulness of God stood out in the sign of the rainbow. The Divine promise was necessary to man. It was an assured hope for the future.

Noah Got Drunk

Who would believe Noah got drunk (Genesis 9:21)? What happened? It was a matter of the fertilization process. Before the Flood, the canopy acted as a type of cap. The barometric pressure was lowered considerably after the Flood. The higher air pressure slowed the release of CO_2, which slowed the fertilization process. Noah got caught off-guard. It took wine longer to ferment before the Flood. When the canopy disappeared, the fermentation rate of wine accelerated because of lower air pressure. Noah was unaware of this. He drank the same amount of wine after the Flood as he did before, but it did not inebriate him.

Today, drunkenness occurs more rapidly at higher elevations - where the air pressure is not as great - than at sea level.

Nimrod

Nimrod means, "the rebel." The two kingdoms he founded, Babylon and Assyria, were eventual conquerors of the nation of Israel. "He began to be mighty on the earth" is understood to mean he struggled to achieve power. Nimrod is described twice in Genesis 10:9. It should read "a mighty hunter in the face of the LORD." It is understood from Jewish tradition and from extra-biblical sources that Nimrod was an evil tyrant who hunted both men and animals and rebelled against the LORD. Though Nimrod is not mentioned in Genesis 11, from Chapter 10 we learn that he founded Babel. Read Genesis 11:1-9.

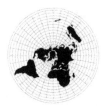

THE TOWER OF BABEL

The first event of worldwide significance recorded in the Bible after the Great Flood was the rebellion at the Tower of Babel.

The Tower of Babel was to be the masterpiece of world architecture. Records reveal that over 26 tons of gold were used in its construction. Babel was to be the political and religious capital of the then known world - a place reaching into the heavens (Genesis 11:4). This was not a literal climbing up into the heavens, but making contact with the spiritual realm - the fallen spiritual world. Fallen man had learned how to contact the fallen demonic realm. God saw what fallen man was attempting and stopped it (Genesis 11:6-8).

The Tower of Babel narrative in Genesis 11:1-9 is not a myth. Those who claim it is a myth are mythsaken. This account is literal history. The Babel crisis occurred some 300 years after the Flood. They all spoke one language, no doubt the Hebrew language. The term "words" refers to the content of their speech. They had the same vocabulary. "Hand me another brick" meant just that. The Tower of Babel explains why the world's people groups speak different languages. God created the languages. The whole earth (refers to the people who lived on the earth) had a common language and a common vocabulary. Genesis 10 has the 70 nations arranged by languages. It is part of the narrative art of Genesis to give the explanation of the event after the narration of the event. From this time onward Babel, or Babylon, becomes the symbol-city of "this present evil world," stimulated by the arch-rebel, Satan.

The people found a plain in the land of Shinar and settled there. A plain is flat land. They could not have built such a tall structure on a curved earth spinning at 1,038 mph. The tower rose to a height of 153 feet above the plain from a base covering a square of 400 feet, or almost four acres. It was constructed of kiln-dried bricks in seven stages to correspond with the 7 planets visible to the naked eye. The seven levels were dedicated to the planets and color coded. The lowest level was black, the color of Saturn; the next orange, for Jupiter; the third red, for Mars. On the summit of the tower were the signs of the Zodiac and other astrological figures.

God intended the confusion of languages to scatter the human race from one location. The stream of civilization follows the newly developed languages. Nations arose from the groups who spoke the same language. Wherever Archaeology has discovered a civilization they learn that man always used a written communication system, utilized fire, built family dwellings, played music, and practiced religion.

Pyramids

Shortly after the building of the Tower of Babel and the dividing of the nations, pyramids began to be built around the world. God divided the people into language groups. When the language groups scattered throughout the world, they started to duplicate the Tower of Babel, constructing pyramid-like structures. Thousands of these pyramid forms have been found throughout the world.

Post-Flood mankind knew who the true God was. From Noah's three sons, everyone was told the story about the deluge and that it was an act of judgment by God. Noah was still living during Abraham's life. Shem, Noah's son, was still alive during Jacobs's day. But man, because of his pride and human foolishness worshiped the creation rather than the Creator.

The Apostle Paul explained how the true story told by the sons of Noah became perverted and mankind began to worship idols - the stars. Read: Romans 1:21-23.

Astrology vs Astronomy

Astrology is a pseudoscience that claims to have divine information about human affairs and terrestrial events by studying the movements and relative positions of celestial objects. Astrological people are self-centered and hot-tempered. Everything is about "me, me, me." Astrology corrupted the 12 signs of the Zodiac.

Astrology is a pseudoscience based on the view that the stars and planets exert a strong influence on human affairs. Astrology is a dangerous and wrongful practice. God created stars as a calendar and for declaring God's glory. To consult the stars is idolatry. Astrology should not be consulted for amusement. It is connected with the force of evil, occult practices, and bondage to sin. Reading the horoscope is bad because people who believe in star signs are more likely to be impulsive instead of being levelheaded in making choices.

Scripture warns against the practice of astrology. See Daniel 4:19; 2 Kings 23:5; and Isaiah 47:13. Christians are called to consult the Word of God, commanded to pray without ceasing, and seek the wisdom of wise men.

You will not find a real solution for your problems by consulting a horoscope. This is a worldly means. A person's root problem is a sinful nature. A horoscope is an astrological chart or diagram representing the positions of the Sun, Moon, and planets.

Astronomy is the branch of science which deals with celestial objects, space, and the physical cosmos as a whole. Science means knowledge. Mazzarot is a Hebrew word found in the Book of Job. Its literal meaning is a Garland of Crowns.

The text in Genesis 11:4 should have been translated a representation of the heavens, instead of 'a top which reached unto heaven.' The Babel tower was designed to hand down antediluvian traditions. The description suggests a massive effort motivated by pride (Isaiah 2:15-17). What was wrong with what they were doing? The fact that its builders were defying the Divine command to scatter, to spread abroad and replenish the earth. They sacrilegiously challenged God. They disobeyed the Cultural Mandate first given to Adam and Eve (Genesis 1:28), and given again to Noah and his three sons, Ham, Shem, and Japheth (Genesis 9:1). They began to build a city and a tower to make a name for themselves. They wanted fame and offspring. God gives an everlasting name only to those who magnify His name, not to those who attempt self-assertion. They refused to be dispersed over the face of the whole earth. The expression 'face of the earth' refers to the earth being a flat plane. The face of a map and of a clock are flat. The face of a person is considered flat, with some high and low places.

The LORD came down to see what was going on. Divine judgment is always according to truth. The Mesopotamian ziggurat towers (a rectangular stepped tower surrounded by a temple) were built as descending stairways for the pagan gods. But the Triune God held a committee meeting. "Come, let us (Hebrew: Elohim, a masculine plural noun; God is one living God, Who exists in three co-eternal and co-substantial persons: the Father, the Son, and the Spirit) go down and there confuse their language, so that they may not understand one another's speech. So the LORD (Elohim) dispersed them from there over the face (flat earth) of all the earth, and they left off building the city. Therefore its name was called Babel, because there the LORD confused the language of all the earth. And from there the LORD dispersed them over the face of all the flat earth. The etymology of the Hebrew word means "confuse." To the Babylonians, Babel means "gate of god." Babel was the capital of Nimrod's kingdom. Nimrod, a rebel, founded the ancient cities of Babylon and Ninevah. They were two great cities.

The confusion of language (Genesis 11:1-9) was a control operation. The increasing of human languages was a terminating restraint. It was hurried along by a human alliance to establish the first united nations - a big group center, with a high celestial tower. Verse 4 does not suggest the height of the tower. What it says is , "And its top with the heavens." Not "with its top in the heavens." The tower was a museum with an astronomical planisphere, Zodiac pictures, and drawings of the constellations. A planisphere is a representation of the circles of the sphere on a plane; a polar projection of the celestial sphere and stars on a plane.

Peleg's Prophecy

In Genesis 10:25 we are told that it was in Peleg's days that "the earth was divided." This happened at the division of languages at Babel. Peleg died 349 years after the Flood. This name comes from the Hebrew verb for "separate" or "divide." Peleg prophesied the dispersal of the nations at Babel. In Psalm 55:9, the same Hebrew verb is used for a division of languages

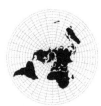

STREAMS OF CIVILIZATION

Noah had three sons: Ham, Shem, and Japheth.

HAM formed the nations of Africa.

SHEM formed the nations of the east (China).

JAPHETH formed the European nations.

They scattered in all directions according to language. God did not breakup families, clans and tribes with language barriers. The descendants of Ham spoke similar languages and dialects, the descendants of Shem spoke similar languages and dialects, and the descendants of Japheth spoke similar languages and dialects.

The Museum of the Alphabet in Waxhaw, NC traces the history of writing. Find out where your alphabet came from. A visit at the Museum of the Alphabet transports you around the world where displays throughout 12 rooms trace the history of the world's alphabets, from cuneiform to tonal languages to Native American language syllabaries. A syllabary is a set of written symbols that represent the syllables or moras which make up words.

Explore other writing systems such as mathematics, music, and Braille. Learn modern stories of communities being transformed through literacy and Bible translation.

More than 600 million people speaking roughly 5,100 languages have less than a full New Testament in the language they value most. And when they can't understand what they read or hear, the life-transforming power of the gospel is stopped in its tracks. JAARS is doing something about that.

https://www.jaars.org/experience/museums/

The Adam and Eve Family

Adam named his wife Eve, because she would become the "Mother of All the Living" (Genesis 3:20). According to Jewish historian Josephus, the number of Adam and Eve's children, as the old Rabbinical tradition says, was 56. Thirty-three (33) sons, and twenty-three (23) daughters. Three of their sons include Cain, Abel, and Seth. One of the daughters was Cain's wife.

What language did Adam and Eve speak? Probably Hebrew, although the Bible does not say. When Jesus appeared to Saul on the road to Damascus, He spoke to him in the Hebrew language (Acts 9:1-6; 26:12-14). Genesis 5:5 says Adam lived a total of 930 years, and then he died. Eve probably lived a total of 930 years as well.

How tall were Adam and Eve? According to calculations, Adam and Eve were 15 feet tall. That was a tall fall.

Cain and Abel—Genesis 4

Cain and Abel were brothers, the first two sons of Adam and Eve. Cain was a farmer. Abel was a shepherd. They both gave offerings. The lamb was the designated offering to be given. Cain may have meant well, but he was not following God's directions. Abel's offering was accepted and Cain's offering was rejected. Why? Cain's offering was the fruit of his labors. Abel's offering was a lamb. There is some scriptural indication that the offering was consumed by fire from heaven. They both recognized that their offering was accepted or rejected. Cain's envy and hatred of his brother Abel led to murder. Cain murdered Abel. The first murder. Both brothers had the same parents. They were fallen parents. Both of them were outside of Eden, so they were judicially alienated. All human beings are judicially alienated. They had a differing basis for offering. Cain's offering was of his own works - the fruit of a cursed ground. Abel's offering anticipates the willing offering of Jesus Christ, the perfect Lamb of God. Cain - his own works vs. the completed work of Christ on the cross. Only the acceptable offerings to God are acceptable.

Hebrews 9:22 states, "and without the shedding of blood there is no forgiveness of sins." God is very specific on His specifications. Death was required. It was the substitutionary death of the lamb that pointed to the substitutionary death on our behalf. God would provide (Genesis 22:14). That was emblematic of that which occurred on the cross.

Where did Cain get his wife? He married his brother's sister because he was able. Adam and Eve had many sons and daughters. There was a significant population at that time. As the years went by, with extreme longevity, there was a large population. So much so, that Cain was in fear of being attacked. That's why God gave him special protection.

The Myth Racial Classification

American anthropologist Carleton S. Coon divided humanity into five so-called races in the mid-20th century. First, there is only one race - the human race. There is only humankind, not human species. There are species of plants, fish, birds, animals, and small creatures or creepy-crawly critters, not humans. The term 'race' divides humans according to physical characterizes that are inherited. Human racial types are based on visual traits or how a person looks - outward appearances (such as skin tone, cranial (skull shape), facial features, or type of hair).

The five so-called races are:

1. Caucasoid (White) race
2. Negroid (Black) race
3. Capoid (Bushmen/Hottentots) race
4. Mongoloid (Oriental / Amerindian) race
5. Australoid (Australian Aborigine) race

Carleton Coon made up these five categories. These five racial classifications do not exist, except in the mind of secular scientists who believe all humans evolved from a lower life form. From 'goo' to you by way of the zoo. There's only one race, not five. These five categories divide humanity, not unite. This myth ranks human beings by promoting superior races and demoting inferior races. Dividing the human race into categories leads to racism. What is racism? It is an attitude of prejudice, discrimination, and antagonism directed against a person or people groups on the basis of their skin shade or how they look. Skin colors are not red and yellow, black and white, only brown: light brown, mid-brown, and dark brown skin.

How we treat others is the essence of "ethics." Biblical theology and ethics are co-extensive. There is no greater commandment than loving God and loving one another. (Mark 12:29-31). If we love God, we love our neighbors.

Having the attitude that you are my brother from another mother is life-changing. All people come from the same human family - Adam's race. We all share the same gene pool. We are all related going back to the "Mother of All the Living," Eve. True love does not judge a person on the basis of their skin tone. Jesus said, "This is my commandment: Love each other in the same way I have loved you" (John 15:12).

> "Man looks on the outward appearance,
> but the Lord looks on the heart."
> *1 Samuel 16:7*

Melanin

The amount of melanin pigment in humans determines their skin tone. God made one race, the human race. God made all people of one skin color - brown, not red, or yellow, or black, or white skin. Skin tones range from dark brown to middle brown to light brown. Brown is the color, tone is the various shades of brown. Welcome to the Brown family.

The DNA of Adam and Eve produced a middle brown skin tone (AaBb).

Genes For Melanin

Multiple combinations of the genetic code:

1. AABB + aabb genes = AaBb genes of "middle brown" skin shade.
2. AABB genes + AABB genes = of dark-skinned offspring.
3. AaBb genes + AaBb genes = of wide range of skin colors.
4. aabb genes + aabb genes = of light-skinned offspring.

Some Fundamental Questions

Is the cosmos 15 billion years old? No.

Hubble Telescope - *Do we see 100's of light years away?* No. *Do we see galaxies that are 100s of light years away?* No. *Did that light start traveling 100 billion years ago?* No. *Does this prove we live in an old universe?* No.

The Bible says the cosmos was created in six days.

6 days x 24 hours = 144 hours. *Are the days 24 hour days?* Yes.

Were the aging factors built in? Yes. Trees created with tree rings. When God breathed into Adam's nostrils the breath of life, the man became a living soul. Adam was fully developed physically, able to stand up, move about, and speak. (Genesis 2:7). God programmed Adam with knowledge.

Was a galaxy created to look like it's 100 billion light years away? No. "Let light be" instantly sent electromagnetic waves into the cosmos. The cosmos was fully visible, even without the sun, moon, and stars.

Actually, space is not as big as secular science claims. After God stretched out the heavens, the stretching process was completed. Space is not expanding, no matter what Einstein said. He was wrong. The first quote of God was, "Let light be." And it was so. Light was present everywhere when God spoke. God is light. God is omnipresent - everywhere present. Light is omnipresent. When God said, "Let light be," there was no waiting factor for the light to appear on earth. "It was so" means it appeared everywhere in a flash.

The "days" of Genesis were not geological eras. No matter how many science degrees or theology degrees a person may have earned, they cannot justify claiming that Theistic evolution was the mechanism God used to create. Evolution is denied by Scripture in many ways. Mixing theology with evolution is like mixing forks and power outlets. Dangerous. God is not an evolutionist. Creation was supernatural and instantaneous. When God spoke, He did not say, "Let evolution begin." Evolution was not the mechanism God used to create.

PLANE TRIGONOMETRY

Ready for a pure mathematics lesson? In high school we studied plane geometry and plane trigonometry. An equilateral triangle is a triangle with all three sides of equal length. In mathematics, a plane is a flat, two-dimensional surface that extends infinitely far. It is known as a two-dimensional surface. It's called plane geometry because the earth is a plane, a flat surface, not a convex surface. A plane has zero curvature, infinite width, infinite length, and varying depth. We learned the angles of a triangle add up to 180° and no more. The shapes of triangles vary: 30 + 60 + 90 = 180, or 45 + 45 + 90 = 180.

The Nature of Reality

A glimpse of hyperspace. Hyperspace is a word for describing spaces of more than three dimensions. Scientific evolutionists claim that since we have encountered the curvature of the earth it allows a triangle to add up to more than 180° in hyperspace. This is pseudoscience. There is a big problem here. Their presumption is wrong. The earth is not a globe. The curvature of the earth does not exist. We inhabit a space of three dimensions with height, width and depth, well known for centuries. Well known until Einstein came along. We cannot consider time as an additional fourth dimension. We do not live in four dimensions, only three. A four dimensional world is a world of Einstein's fantasy; an imaginary world. Einstein added time to justify the heliocentric model.

A triangle with more than 180° is a violation of Euclidean geometry. Euclid, a 4th century Greek mathematician, was the father of geometry. His Elements is one of the most influential works in the history of mathematics. The Elements begins with plane geometry - a triangle has only 180°. Plane geometry and plane trigonometry are called plane because the earth is a plane with a flat surface. A triangle of more than 180° is not true geometry.

To become an airplane pilot or seaman you must go to school to study navigation, and take a course in spherical trigonometry.

The evolutionary science teachers claim that we are dealing with a convex surface, and therefore you can have 90° in three corners. Spherical (3-D) trigonometry violates the rule of plane geometry. They are playing with a dimension that does not exist, but they teach it as though it does. Evolution is a lie and evolutionists lie to support their lie. Here, Einstein entered the sphere of non-Euclidean geometry. However, non-Euclidean geometry is not real. Einstein invented it ex nihilo. You can go in circles until you are dizzy studying curved surfaces, but you can never justify a triangle having more than 180° or that the earth is a curved ball spinning on a tilted axis at 1,038 mph.

Einstein's Revolution

Albert Einstein developed his Special Relativity theory in 1905. He claimed that length, mass, velocity and time are relative to the velocity of the observers. Velocity means speed.

He developed General Relativity in 1915. Here he claimed that there is no distinction between time and space = a 4-dimensional continuum. He was wrong. There is a difference between time and space. Space is real and fundamental. Time is a mental construct.

God is outside of time. There are no clocks or calendars in Heaven. In the beginning God created time, space and matter for man. These three properties came into existence at the same time, but they are different.

The Nature of Time

Time is linear. Point A is the beginning of someone or something and point B is the ending. Time is like an arrow. Time moves forward. We look back and live in the present. We look back and move forward. We cannot move back. God sees time as the past, the present, and the future at the same time. The name Yahweh Elohim is greater than the concepts of space, time, and number.

Entropy

In physics, entropy is interrupted as the degree of disorder or randomness in the system. Increasing entropy is increasing randomness. The cosmos is moving from order to disorder. The second law of thermodynamics says that entropy always increases with time. Only God can create order out of disorder. Genesis 1:2 says the earth was "without form and void." An empty unfinished house is without form and void. The framework is there. For six 24-hour days, God the Master Builder "built" everything that exists as we know it. The Hebrew Phrase, Tohu wa-bohu meaning "without form and void" is an expression of the first stage of the creative progress during the first day. Tohu wa-bohu or "without form and void" does not imply or support the gap theory. The gap between Genesis 1:1 and 1:2 is a lie.

The Nature of God

God is not subject to the restrictions of mass, acceleration or density (gravity) in space. God is not simply One with "lots of time" on His hands. He is outside the restrictions of time. This uniqueness is His Personal imprint. God is outside time.

> "For thus says the One who is high and lifted up,
> who inhibits eternity, whose name is Holy."
> *Isaiah 57:15 ESV*

God has the capacity to create us, and the means to get a message to us that we know is authentic. This is prophecy. God writes history in advance. Some examples: The Golden Image of Nebuchadnezzar in Daniel 2. The history of the rise and fall of ancient Israel. The Messiahship of Jesus Christ prophesied in the OT and authenticated in the NT.

"Declaring the end from the beginning and from ancient times
things not yet done, saying, 'My counsel shall stand,
and I will accomplish all my purpose."
Isaiah 46:10 ESV

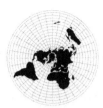

THE GEOMETRY OF ETERNITY

The geometry of eternity is a straight line in space from infinity to infinity. That line is not curved in a three dimensional space coming at us. Eternity is not a curved line. That's Einstein's pseudoscience. Behind us is the past, today is the present, and ahead of us is the future. For humans, life is a sequence of events in time. God can see the past, present, and future simultaneously from His perspective in Heaven. Like riding in a helicopter above a parade, you can see what's going on from the beginning all the way to the end at the same time.

The cosmos as a whole is a time-space-matter continuum. Space is length, breadth, and depth. Time is past, present, and future. Matter is cause, event, and consequence (energy, motion, and phenomenon). We exist in space, which is manifested in matter and understood in time.

The Trinity is E Pluribus Unum or "Out of Many, One." God is unity with diversity - Father, Son, and Spirit. God is unity and the Trinity is diversity. Christian doctrine teaches that God is Triune. God is a unity, not a unit. God reveals Himself as a Tri-Unity; a Three-Unity or Trinity. Jesus explicitly claimed to be equal with God.

Christians are monotheists, not polytheists. The Trinity can be explained as multiplied wholeness. The math formula is: $1 \times 1 \times 1 = 1$. Christians do not believe that the explanation is adding units. The math formula is not: $1 + 1 + 1 = 3$.

In The Name

The Great Commission, which is recorded in Matthew 28:16-20, commissions believers to go and make disciples of all nations. In other words, Christianize the nations. Save souls and cultures. We're commissioned to baptize them in the name of the Father and of the Son and of the Holy Spirit. This is incorrect grammar, but correct theology. Notice the word 'name' is singular before a plural list. It's not 'in the names' of each person of the Godhead. The singular word 'name' includes equally the three persons in the Trinity. Shema. The LORD is one (Deuteronomy 6:4). God is unity with diversity.

God is ontological. Like the wind, God is an invisible Spirit being with reality. God is unseen realness. God is One God, and yet He is Father, Son, and Spirit. God is Father in generation, Son in declaration, and Spirit in appropriation. Sounds like a three-point sermon.

In Six Days

"For in six days the LORD made heaven and earth, the seas,
and all that is in them, and rested on the seventh day."
Exodus 20:11 ESV

God cannot lie. He spoke these words in the middle of the Ten Commandments.

IN THE STARS HIS HANDIWORK I SEE

Yahweh named the stars and organized them into their constellations and called those constellations out by name.

"He determines the number of the stars (in each constellation)
and calls them (the constellations) each by name."
Psalm 147:4

Did you know the stars sing together? In the key of B flat. Low B flat below low C. Scientists have listened to the stars concert of praise.

The Hebrew word translated "sky" and "heaven" is shamayim, which means "the place in the sky where the stars are located" referring specifically to the Zodiac. Shamayim is plural, which means heavens.

Mazzaroth/Zodiac

The English words "heaven" or "sky" or "firmament" refer to the Book of the Mazzaroth (the Zodiac). Yahweh stretched out the "heavens" or Zodiac signs like a scroll across the ecliptic plane (the path of the Sun).

Mazzaroth is a Hebrew Word found in the Book of Job and literally means a Garland of Crowns, but its context is that of Astronomical Constellations, and it is often interpreted as a term for the Zodiac or the Constellations. The word Zodiac comes from the Greek word ZOAD meaning "a way, a step, a circuit, a circle."

"Can you lead forth the Mazzaroth in their season,
or can you guide the Bear with its children?"
Job 38:32 ESV

Brown-Driver-Briggs - 8064. shamayim - 1.a. visible heavens, sky, where stars, etc., are. Judges 5:20, Genesis 15:5, Deuteronomy 4:19

"This is what Yahweh says - your Redeemer, who formed you in
the womb: I am Yahweh, the Maker of all things, who stretches
out the heavens" *(like a scroll, i.e., Mazzaroth/Zodiac).*
Isaiah 44:24

The Zodiac is stretched out in the heavens, the 12 signs created by Yahweh (Zodiac Signs) are laid out across the ecliptic plane like a scroll and read like a pictograph in order as the Sun goes through each sign each year. The signs proclaim the Plan of Salvation.

Genesis 1:14 informs us that the stars are to be for signs, seasons, days and years. Signs are markers that give us information of upcoming events. These signs are given to us by the names of the stars and order of the constellations. Signs are not given to be used in a perverted way that is used today in Astrology. False religion has conditioned us to believe the Mazzaroth/Zodiac is evil; and that we should not even seek out the message within it.

The late Dr. D.J. Kennedy, evangelical pastor of Coral Ridge Presbyterian Church in Fort Lauderdale, Florida, wrote a book entitled The Real Meaning of the Zodiac, in which he proved that God created the Zodiac! God intended the stars to foretell the future of the world. In his sermon entitled, The Gospel in the Stars, he explained that the real meaning of the Zodiac was to reveal God's plan of salvation in Christ. He also denounced using horoscopes. He taught that the stars point to the Creator.

It was Yahweh who created the Zodiac; He brought forth the starry hosts and constellations one by one and named them.

> "Lift up your eyes and look to the heavens: Who created all
> these? He who brings out the starry host *(Signs of the Zodiac)*
> one by one and calls forth each of them by name."
> *Isaiah 40:26*

The Bible tells us over and over again to "look up to the heavens" because they communicate the Gospel message of salvation that gives hope to fallen humanity. Psalm 147:4 and Isaiah 40:26 make it clear that it was Yahweh who named the stars and constellations to write a prophetic message in them concerning the redemption of humanity. The names of the stars and groupings of stars has been known since creation in 4004 B.C. The 12 constellations begin with Virgo, which means "VIRGIN." The message of the Zodiac begins with Virgo and ends with Leo the Lion.

Before clocks, time or seasons of the year was known only by the constellations passing overhead or the constellation the Sun was in. In Job 38:32 Yahweh asked, "Can you bring forth Mazzaroth (the 12 signs) in their season?" The 12 signs form the path that the Sun takes in the heavens, namely the Zodiac. Psalm 19:6 states that "(the Sun) goes from one end of heaven, and its circuit (or path, i.e., Zodiac) is to the other end of it. In Psalm 19:4-6 we learn that Yahweh established a dwelling place for the Sun. The Sun is described as the Heavenly Bridegroom, who comes forth (moving) to run his race and returns to his place of origin. It is apparent from Psalm 19 and other passages that the Sun represents Yeshua, the heavenly Bridegroom.

Real Time History

When God's special star led the wisemen to Bethlehem, the little sleepy village was occupied territory. Sixty years earlier, the Roman army had marched through the region claiming Palestine as a Roman province. Roman legions were busy conquering new territories.

Emperor Nero was a megalomaniac. That's a big word for power-hungry. It's a fact of history, Nero fiddled while Rome burned. No doubt, his violin wasn't a

Stradivarius. The exact area destroyed by the great fire of A.D. 64 conveniently cleared a section of the city that Nero wanted for the building of his lavish palace. To deflect the blame, Nero pinned the arson on the new sect of Christians. The false charge launched the first great persecution of Christians in the Roman Empire. What goes around comes around. Nero was forced by his own officials to commit suicide in A.D. 68.

Daniel, the Chief Astrologer

The Bible calls those who use divination techniques to seek counsel from Yahweh... Prophets. Those who use divination and seek counsel for other gods...false prophets, soothsayers, etc.

The Prophet Daniel was the "Chief Astrologer" in the Babylonian Court. Daniel was a Eunuch; thus, he did not have any children or heirs. He accumulated a huge fortune serving at the highest levels of various empires and kings. Serving as their 'advisor' or chief astrologer, Daniel became the right-hand man of the kings who considered Daniel as King "by proxy." Daniel became one of the most powerful and wealthy men across several dynasties and kings. Daniel trained the Chaldean astrologers on how to properly understand the Zodiac and how it foretold of the coming King Messiah. He gave specific instructions to those in his 'school of astrology' on how to find the newborn King using God's GPS system - astrology and signs in the sky / Zodiac (defined in Revelation 12, a sign in the constellation Virgo that announced the birth of the King).

Daniel's prophesy is dated in the first year of King Darius, which means that it was written in the year 539 B.C., about 66 or 67 years after the Jews initially went into exile to Babylonia.

When Yeshua was born in Bethlehem Ephrathah (Micah 5:2), the messianic expectation was at a high-level all-over Israel. The people all knew it was time that the Messiah would be born according to Daniel's prophecies. The Messiah was born at the right time and on time (Galatians 4:4). The only ones who came seeking the Christ-child were astrologers. Only those who knew how to read the Zodiac signs found him. The Bible calls these astrologers "wise men" ...trained by Daniel. These astrologers, more than three in number, brought to the new born King the wealth of several Empires passed down through the centuries from

Daniel. It was a King's ransom to the new born Messiah. That historic day, Mary and Joseph became extremely wealthy parents.

> Behold, a virgin shall give birth to a son.
> *Isaiah 7:14; Matthew 1:23*

The sign of a "woman giving birth to a son/king" among the stars was when Jupiter moved into the womb of the constellation Virgo. Once Jupiter was inside the "womb" of Virgo, it went into retrograde motion and literally bounced around inside the womb of Virgo for exactly nine months (the time of human gestation). Then Jupiter exited out of the birthing canal (between the legs of Virgo). Revelation 12 speaks of the "woman giving birth" and "birth pains" which describes the "sign in the Zodiac" in detail.

Yeshua was born in late September (not December 25) when the sun was moving through Virgo, and she would be "clothed with the sun" as Revelation 12 describes. This is how the Chaldean astronomers knew when to begin seeking for the birth of the Messiah. They knew the exact year He would be born. Daniel taught the Chaldean astrologers the meaning of Ages and when the next Age should occur. They knew the general timing because He was to be born during the transition from the Age of Aries to the Age of Pisces. When they saw the "sign of the son of man" approaching, they knew He would be born in the Fall of September the year Jupiter entered the womb of Virgo with the Sun at her back and the moon at her feet. They knew to find Him in Bethlehem Ephrathah because it was prophesied in Micah 5:2. There were two villages named Bethlehem in Israel, but only one with the second name Ephrathah.

FAILURE OF GENTILES TO REACH THE DIVINE IDEAL

"The wrath of Yahweh" is being revealed from heaven *(the place where the stars are located, i.e., the Zodiac)* against all the godlessness and wickedness of people, who suppress the truth *(of its message)* by the wickedness *(and worship the signs of the Zodiac, Sun, Moon, and stars)*, since what may be known about Yahweh *(the Plan of Salvation)* is plain to them *(is proclaimed in the Zodiac)*, because Yahweh has made it plain to them *(this message goes out unto all the Earth - Psalm 19, given to all mankind - Deuteronomy 3:19)*. For since the creation of the world *(written in the stars at Creation)* Yahweh's invisible qualities - his eternal power and divine nature - have been clearly seen *(in the Zodiac, as Yahweh witnessed the Gospel to Abraham - Genesis 15:5)*, being understood *(they are metaphors and analogies)* from what has been make *(in heaven: the Sun , the Moon, the stars, and constellations - Psalm 119)*, so that people are without excuse. For although they knew Yahweh *(is the Creator)*, they neither glorified him as Elohim nor gave thanks to him *(for the message proclaimed in the Zodiac)*, but their thinking became futile *(understanding the*

Zodiac literally as gods) and their foolish hearts were darkened
(to worship the creation over the Creator). Although they claimed
to be wise *(through philosophy and mythology)*, they became
fools and exchanged the glory of the immortal Elohim *(the Glory of
Yahweh is Yeshua - 2 Corinthians 4:6. So they exchanged Yeshua)*
for images made to look like mortal human beings *(solar demigods)* and birds and animals and reptiles" *(the signs of the Zodiac)*.
Romans 1:18-23

No Excuse to Be An Atheist

"For his invisible attributes namely, his eternal power
and divine nature, have been clearly perceived, ever since
the creation of the world, in the things that have been made,
So they are without excuse."
Romans 1:20 ESV

Worship the Creator

Yahweh declared it was He who named all the stars, and brought forth each constellation (12) by name, and they proclaim a message that goes out to all the Earth
(Psalm 19:1-2). The Zodiac was not a creation of the Greeks. The Greeks dreamed
up a system of mythology around the Zodiac that worshiped the creation over the
Creator. Paul wrote to the Greeks in Rome. The Apostle to the Gentiles warned
them against this very thing.

The 'heavens' which is the Zodiac (stars and 12 constellations) proclaim the
Glory of Yahweh. Psalm 19:1 tells us the heavens (the Mazzaroth/Zodiac) declare
the glory of Yahweh. That "glory of Yahweh" is that they proclaim the coming
Messiah Yeshua as He is the "glory of Yahweh" His Father (2 Corinthians 4:6).

Signs of the Zodiac

Each of the stars and 12 constellations have names. The way to know the names
of the stars in the Zodiac is to know the order of their brightness. The secret is to

know the star names in Hebrew. Getting back to the ancient names is necessary to learn what the names infer. It is the key to understanding what the message of the Zodiac confers, from Virgo (the Virgin) to Leo, the Lion of the tribe of Judah. God put the message of redemption in the constellations of the stars. Scholars say Adam and Enoch read this message and explained it to their children by the use of mnemonics, a memory device. A mnemonic is a learning technique that aids in the retention of information.

Galaxy Lights

When God said, "Let light be" in Genesis 1:3, light became everywhere present in the universe. It was instantaneous.

God is:	Light is:
Eternal (always existed)	Eternal (always existed)
Light	Light
Omnipresent	Omnipresent
Invisible	Invisible
Energy	Energy
Bright	Bright

God is omnipresent. He is everywhere present. You cannot escape from His presence (Psalm 139:7-10). Heaven, earth, the depths, He is there. When God said, "Let light be," it did not have to travel millions of light years to reach earth. God is omnipresent and light is omnipresent. Adam was created on Friday. On that first Friday night, Adam saw the Friday night lights on display. They had been shining since Thursday. And light was everywhere on Thursday, not millions of light years away. Remember, God is light (1 John 1:5). In fact, God is the Father of lights, with whom is no variableness (the quality of being subject to variation), neither shadow of turning (James 1:17). The furthest galaxies and the closest galaxies released their light at the same time. There was no time delay. There was no variableness in light travel on the fourth day, or shadow of turning. Yes, light travels at 186,000 miles per second, but to begin with, light appeared everywhere instantaneously. Everything God created, plants, grass, trees, vegetation, fish, birds, animals, insects, critters, and man were fully mature, including light. God created light mature and fully present. God never heard of millions of light years. That's a Darwinian evolutionary idea. That's man's calculations. The furthest galaxy and the closest galaxy have the same twist which says they were created at the same time. God created all the stars and the galaxies on the fourth day. Batteries were included.

Job 38:19 asks, "What is the way to the abode of light?" Where is the way to the home of light? Light is dynamic; darkness is static. Job 38:31 asks, "Can you bind the chains (sweet influences) of the Pleiades, or loose the bands of Orion?" These two are the only visible to the eye constellations in direct electromagnetic radiation bondage to each other. God put belts of bondage around His stars and planets. WARNING: Do not enter! Like the Moon, for instance. In physics, electromagnetic radiation consists of waves propagating through space carrying energy, which includes radio waves, microwaves, infrared, light, ultraviolet, X-rays, and gamma rays. All of these waves form part of the electromagnetic spectrum. In heaven we will be able to see the full spectrum of light and all its multi colors. Heaven will be in technicolor. Beauty beyond imagination.

Signs in the Heavens

Mazzaroth (Zodiac) are signs of God's plan of redemption (Job 38:12). The Hebrew Mazzaroth is what we call the Zodiac. Groups of stars have names. Their names are a way of locating them in the second heaven. They have had their names since creation. There are 12 classical clusters or constellations of stars that are on the ecliptic. There is the actual path of the sun through the sky in a year, as described in Psalm 19:4b-6. That's the ecliptic. The sun's path is not apparent. That's heliocentric speak.

There are two places where the ecliptic crosses the celestial equator which is called the equinox. That's when the days and nights are equal length. The winter solstice marks the first day of winter. It is the shortest day of the year around December 21. Our days are determined where the sun is in its path. Nothing else.

Ready for a little evolution? A big lie? Start: The winter solstice occurs when either of Earth's poles reaches its maximum tilt away from the Sun. This happens twice yearly, once in each hemisphere. End. The earth is not tilted on an axis and does not spin. The earth is not a round ball. The earth is a flat plane, and God hangs the earth in space on nothing (Job 26:7). North is north, earth is not tilted off true north at 23.4 degrees.

We do not know the number of stars in the sky. God knows. All the stars have a name. Psalm 147:4 and Isaiah 40:26 tell us God calls them each by name. Wow!

The word Zodiac comes from the Greek word Sodi, which means "the Way." Not the way or path of the sun, but an allusion of God's plan of redemption. Early followers of Christ were believers who belonged to the Way. "The Way" is mentioned several times in the Book of Acts. See: 9:2; 19:9, 23: 22:4; 24:14, 22. God put "the Way" in the constellations. The Zodiac starts with Virgo, the Virgin and ends with Leo, the Lion. Each of the signs of the Zodiac have three decans that are closely associated with it.

THE BATTLE OF THE AGES

The spiritual battle ground is the Zodiac, the Heavenly Scroll. Yahweh Elohim created the stars and the constellations, named them, gave them their meaning, proclaimed the glorious Gospel (Plan of Salvation) in them, and will not give glory to another (Isaiah 44:24; 45:5, 12; 48:5, 8-10). The heavens declare Yahweh's Glory which is Yeshua; not the glory of any other so-called "gods" or "demigods." Yahweh's Glory is Yeshua. Therefore, the heavens (Zodiac) declare Yahweh, not any other pagan demi-god. Any use of the Zodiac that is outside of the Spirit of Yahweh is forbidden.

How Great Thou Art
Stuart K. Hine/Carl Boberg

O Lord my God! when I in awesome wonder
Consider all the worlds Thy hands have made,
I see the stars, I hear the rolling thunder,
Thy power throughout the universe displayed:

Then sings my soul, my Savior God, to Thee.
How great Thou art, how great Thou art!
Then sings my soul, my Savior God, to Thee;
How great Thou art, how great Thou art!

And all God's people said, "AMEN!"

Without Form and Void

Genesis 1:2 says the Earth was without form and void. Earth was unordered and unfilled. There was total darkness over the face of the deep water. Earth was totally covered with cold water. There were not two separate creative acts, with one in Verse 1 and later, the second in Verse 2. The initial creation did not fall into chaos because of the fall of Satan. This is called the Gap Theory. Proponents change the Hebrew word "was" to "became" in terms of without form and void. This refers to creation yet to be formed and filled, not disrepair.

The fall of Satan happened after Adam and Eve were living in the Garden of Eden a while. It could have been 100 years. Satan became jealous that God was spending so much time on Earth with the first couple. He wanted the attention they were getting. After his five prideful "I will's," God cast him out of His heaven (Ezekiel 28:14-17). He fell like lightning to the Earth.

He showed up in the Garden of Eden, which was Paradise on Earth, disguised as a crafty serpent, and lied to Eve about being like God (Genesis 3:1-6). Eve, was naive. She was deceived and yielded to the temptation. Adam and Eve both ate the forbidden fruit, which was an act of direct disobedience to what God had told Adam. 1 Timothy 2:14 says it was not Adam who was deceived, but the woman who was.

"Therefore, just as sin came into the world through one man,
and death through sin, and so death spread to all men
because all sinned."
Romans 5:12 ESV

FACE

In the Bible, face means flat. The face of the deep in Genesis 1:2 suggests that water is level, not curved or bent. Water does not curve or bend, unless it's frozen in something with a curved shape. Like the face of a map and the face of a clock, the face of the liquid water is flat.

Scroll

Revelation 6:14 says the sky was rolled up like a scroll. God unrolled the scroll and stretched out the heavens.

Extremely High Mountain

In the last of the three temptations of Jesus in the wilderness, the devil took Him to the peak of a very high mountain (Matthew 4:8). Why go to the top of an extremely high mountain? It's a matter of perspective. To show Him all the kingdoms of the world and their glory. We're not told where this mountain is located, but Jesus could see the kingdoms of the world from that high vantage point because the Earth is flat. There was nothing to block His view. If the Earth was a globe, He would have only been able to see so far before the horizon dropped off out of His sight.

Without the Earth's curve and from high up: You are able to see large objects more than hundreds of miles away. The Sun and the Moon are 3,100 miles away. We see them everyday. We see the big blue sky everyday. We see the stars twinkle every night.

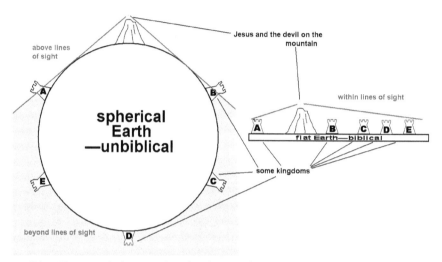

Matthew 4:8: "Again, the devil taketh him up into an exceeding high mountain, and sheweth him all the kingdoms of the world"

Luke 4:5: "And the devil, taking him up into an high mountain, shewed unto him all the kingdoms of the world in a moment of time."

The Chicago skyline can be plainly seen from the Michigan skyline. A picture of the Chicago skyline taken almost 60 miles away is not a mirage. Under normal conditions the skyline is visible. The curvature of the earth is not a factor because the earth is a flat plane. The Chicago skyline is not physically below the horizon from that vantage point because the earth is not a globe. The image of the skyline can be seen at line of sight.

The study of atmospheric refraction (mirage and looming) is pseudoscience, or science so-called. The people who promote the mirage idea are delusional liars.

Firmament, Expanse, Sky, Dome

> And God said, "Let there be an expanse in the midst of the water, and let it separate the waters from the waters."
> *Genesis 1:6*

In the beginning, the whole earth was covered with cold water. God separated the waters by putting the expanse in the middle of the waters, which separated the waters from the waters. Water above and below the expanse.

"And God made the expanse and separated the waters that were under the expanse from the waters that were above the expanse. And it was so. And God called the expanse Heaven."
Genesis 1:7 ESV

Blue Skies

There is water above the dome, that's why the sky is blue. The oceans are blue. Water is blue. The water above the sky was used to flood the earth in the Flood of Noah. God opened the springs of the deep (water underground) and the windows of heaven (floodgates of heaven) to flood the earth (Genesis 8:2). Secular scientists and Bible skeptics and scoffers deny that the Earth was formed out of water and through water by the Word of God, and that by means of these the world that then existed was deluged with water and perished (2 Peter 3:5-6). They deny that there was a worldwide flood on the Earth.

Liquid Water

Earth is covered with 70% water, which averages more than two miles deep. There is as much liquid water under the Earth, the deep, on the surface of the Earth, and above the Sky or Dome today as there was in Genesis 1:2. Liquid water is not vanishing from the Earth. It evaporates into a gas, called water vapor. Condensation, precipitation and evaporation are the three steps in Earth's water cycle. There are 326 million trillion gallons of water on the earth. That's 326 million trillion gallons. Now that's a lot of water. One gallon of water weighs 8.34 pounds. Do the math. If Earth is a round ball, how does the water stay in the oceans rather than splashing into space? There is absolutely no way on earth that all the gallons of water in the oceans could stay within their boundaries if the earth was a globe and spinning at 1,000 mph. No way. It doesn't make any sense. Gravity does not hold the ocean waters within their boundaries. There are four verses about limits for the sea. God set the boundary for the sea. Job 38:10-11; Proverbs 8:29; Psalm 104:9 and Jeremiah 5:22. God said, "This far, but no farther."

Origin of Water

What is the origin of water on Earth? In the beginning God created it. Whom else? What is the history of water on earth? Secular scientists explain that our home Earth "just happened" by chance billions-of-years ago. This pseudoscience. Water first made its grand appearance on the world's stage in Genesis 1:2. Cold dark water covered the whole earth. Then God started the separation process. Hydrogen inside the earth did not play any role in the formation of the oceans, as evolutionists claim. To God be the credit and glory! Earth is unique within the Milky Way galaxy, not a Solar System. Earth is not located in a Solar System. The sun circles above the earth in an elliptical pattern every 24 hours. That's the path or system it follows continually parallel above the earth. Heliocentrists call earth a planet (wanderer) and claim it is located within a Solar System. Earth is not a planet. The word planet means to wander or wanderer. Earth is fixed. It is stationary. It does not move. Earth is not a spinning ball tilted on an axis. Earth is a flat plane. Evolutionists added the letter 't' to the word plane. Plane to planet. Earth is unique because it is the only place in the universe known to have oceans of liquid water on its surface. Water is necessary for life to survive. Liquid water continues to exist on earth because it is located within the Milky Way galaxy in the habitable zone. Not too hot, not too cold. God's purpose in creating the earth was to make it a habitation for man to live in a paradise.

All Heaven and Nature Sing

Does God sing? Zephaniah 3:17 tells us God sings.

> "The LORD your God in your midst, The Mighty One, \
> will save; He will rejoice over you with gladness, He will quiet
> you with His love, He will rejoice over you with singing."
> —NKJV

The Hebrew word for "singing" actually means "a ringing cry" with a sense of joy. The Bible tells us that Elohim gave all of His creatures the ability to sing. Job says the angels, who are also called "stars" in Job, can sing. Stars sing in the key of B flat.

> To what were its foundations fastened? Or who laid its
> cornerstone, when the morning stars sang together,
> and all the sons of God shouted for joy?
>
> —Job 38:6-7 NKJV

Satan and his demons, fallen angels, are never said to sing in the Bible. Sin has a disheartening effect. Sin takes away joy and leaves no desire to sing. People don't sing in godless countries.

Human beings sing, the angels sing, and God sings. God inhabits the praises of His people. The songs recorded in Revelation 5:8-10 and Rev. 15:2-4 give adoration to God. They are directed toward Yahweh Elohim. Praise be to the Highest!

God's Green Earth

Green is the primary color of the flat Earth, because our world vibrates to the 528 Hz frequency. Green is found in the middle of the color scale in a rainbow. Green is the fourth color in every rainbow. The seven colors of the rainbow are: **ROYGBIV**

Frequency

Earth has a frequency. Earth is tuned to the frequency of 432 Hz, which is nature's frequency. 432 Hz is a pitch reference. Birds sing at 432 Hz.

> "In the beginning was the Word, and the Word was with God,
> and the Word was God"
> —John 1:1 ESV

Creatio Ex Logos

In the first chapter of Genesis we read that God spoke everything into existence by the power of His voice—*Creatio Ex Logo*. Elohim created *Ex Logos*, or out of the spoken Word

The spoken Word's voice caused vibrations. Every living thing resounds to the voice of the Creator at the frequency of 432 Hz. Music is the result of sound waves vibrating at different frequencies. Hertz is a unit of frequency. Cycles per second are measured in Hertz. The more vibrations the higher the pitch. Our DNA responds to the frequency of 432 Hz.

A = 432 Hz. is also known as Verdi A tuning or Pythagorean tuning. The 432 Hz. tone is warmer, gentler to the ear, and we can feel the music in our soul. However, the 440 Hertz became the concert standard tuning after WWII.

Sound is essential to life and survival. Our world is full of sounds: birds chirping, insects buzzing about their business, and wind rustling through the trees. On day three of creation week, Elohim, the Intelligent Designer, created green grass, flowers with ears, plants with grain, and trees with fruit (Genesis 1:11-31). God spoke in Genesis 1:11, "Let the earth sprout vegetation, plants yielding seed, and fruit trees bearing fruit in which is their seed, each according to its kind." Plants have the ability to produce food from the sun (photosynthesis). It is a complex biological process. The Creator filled the earth with a large variety and abundance of foods.

Plants hear the buzzing of bees. Flowers produce sweeter nectar in response to the sound vibration frequencies from buzzing of insects. The sound causes flowers to vibrate and makes their nectar 20% sweeter. The bees eat the sweet nectar for nourishment and worker honeybees make honey. Pollen gets on their high-speed wings and when they fly to the next flower, they pollenate it. The bowl-shaped flowers of evening primrose are the key to their acoustic capabilities. The plant neurobiology shows us that they can hear.

Birds sing, whales bellow, and human voices naturally sing at 432 Hz. Birds singing at dawn actually awaken the pores of plants and earth to aid in growth. It's called the Sonic Bloom – musical sounds designed to boost plant growth. There are specific sound frequencies that mimic the dawn chorus of bird song. These frequencies encourage the plants to open their leaf stomata, boosting their intake of morning dew – and gentle organic foliar fertilizers. Birds singing awakens the dawn. Flowers have ears. When the grass and flowers of the field hear the 432 Hz. frequency that the birds are singing early in the morning they know it's time to wake up and start a new day. Rise and shine and give God the glory for it all!

Sound is the vibration of molecules. Air molecules that are set into motion by a vibrating sound source—like bird's voice box—bump into each other. This creates a cascade of movement that we call a pressure wave because it moves outward in bands of increased air pressure. Because the eardrum is sensitive to tiny differences in pressure, we detect the airborne vibrations that enter the ear as sound.

The speed of light, the measurement of the sun and moon are multiplications of 432 Hz. God's creation is truly amazing. Creation is fine-tuned. Everything functions decently and in order.

All of this did not happen by random chance over long periods of time, as Darwinian evolutionists claim. This is not the process of evolution, but of an irreducibly complex creation designed by the Intelligent Designer. None of this would be possible if the shape of the Earth was a round ball tilted on an axis while spinning at 1,038 mph. The Heliocentric Model is absolute nonsense. Nonsense means: preposterous, bizarre, fanciful, foolish, and insane. Stop and think how ridiculous the Heliocentric Model actually is. It's scientifically unprovable and has never been observed. This silly theory is pseudoscience.

When both plants and animals are exposed to music in 432 Hz they grow. The effects of good music on plants include: faster growth, earlier blooms, increased yields, improved nutrition, and reduced pest problems. And there is a boost in sap flow and plant hormones.

The Science of Earthing

According to the charge-neutrality principle, the electric charge of the whole Earth is neutral. God created the electric charge of the whole Earth balanced. All human beings are depleted with negative charges and overloaded with positive charges from poor diet, air pollution's, environmental toxins, insecticides, stress, etc. These abundant positive charges negatively affect our health and well-being. Our cells are like a miniature battery. The human body is both electrical and chemical. We get plenty of positive charges, which can form harmful crystals and cause inflammation. We are extremely lacking negative charges. We do not get the proper negative charge to optimally function. This is known as phase angle. When we lack a full charge, we break down.

What's the solution to this health problem? Grounding. Also called earthing. The science of grounding is a therapeutic technique that involves doing activities that "ground" us to the earth. Electrically reconnecting to the earth is done by simply going barefoot and standing or walking on the grass or sitting or lying on the surface of the flat earth. Walking barefoot will transfer the Earth's electrons from the ground into the body. Electrical charges from the earth will **have** positive effects on your body. Take your synthetic shoes and socks off, go outside, and walk barefoot on the grass for at least 30 minutes twice per day. Sounds too simple? Try it.

Discover the benefits—including better sleep and reduced pain. Walking barefoot or sitting or lying directly on the ground can help pull away flashbacks, unwanted memories, and negative or challenging emotions. Grounding is a practice that will help relieve a panic attack, anxiety, a PTSD flashback, and trauma. You will feel better and have better mental health. Living better is better.

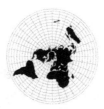

DOCTRINE OF TELEOLOGY

What is teleology? Basically, purpose. It is the doctrine of design and purpose in the material world. It is the branch of philosophy that deals with ends or final causes. "No theory of history can do without teleology." God created on purpose with specific intentions. In general, Scripture teaches that God created the world and all that exists for His own glory and, in particular, made man in His own image (Genesis 1:26) to have fellowship with Him by the exercise of his free will. God so loved the world, not the planets (John 3:16). Christ came down from His glory to save the world of lost men. There are no liquid oceans on the planets, neither is there life of any kind.

Secular scientists deny the doctrine of teleology. In fact, they hate it because it paints God into the picture.

Spinning Wet Ball

If you were to throw a wet tennis ball into the air, the wet ball would spin in flight and the water would splash off. The tennis ball has a small mass, but that has nothing to do with keeping the water on its surface intact.

Gravity or Density?

Isaac Newton did not discover the law of gravity. He invented it. Objects are held on earth by density, not gravity. If an object is heavier than air, it falls to the earth. An apple is heavier than air, that's why it falls off the apple tree to the ground. However, an apple will float on water because water has more density than an apple.

Floating Ax Head

In 2 Kings 6, we read the account of the lost ax head that did swim. The company of prophets with Elisha the prophet went to Jordan to cut down trees to build a bigger place for them to live. But as one was felling a log, his ax head fell into the water. The young lumberjack cried out, "Alas, Master! for it was borrowed." The man of God said, "Where did it fall? When he showed him the place, he cut off a stick and threw it in the water, and made the iron float. He said, "Pick it up." So he reached out his hand and took it. Iron does not float because it's heavier than the density of water. This was a miracle, not magic. God suspended the law of density in this case and floated the ax head to the surface.

The miraculous power of God demonstrates Spiritual truths about God's salvation economy. Examples of supernatural miracles illustrate God's saving power for His people. Such as the ax head of iron floating, parting the Red Sea, manna every morning in the wilderness, stopping the Sun and Moon in the sky for Joshua, turning the Sundial back for Hezekiah, creating new languages at Babel, healing Naamam of leprosy with seven dips in the Jordan River, Jonah saved by being swallowed whole by a big fish, the burning bush, Jesus in the fiery furnace with the three Hebrew friends of Daniel, turning water to the best wine, walking on water, calming the storm, feeding 5,000 people from two fish and five loaves of bread, healing the blind, raising the dead, and casting out devils. These could not have been of a natural occurrence, for no mere man could do these miracles.

Helium

Helium is lighter than air. A balloon filled with helium will float in the air. Helium is a chemical element with the symbol He and atomic number 2. Helium was not formed during the Big Bang, as evolutionists claim. God created it. The Big Bang was a dud. It never exploded.

The Waters

God created the waters on Day One. When God created the earth in Genesis 1:1, it included the waters. Genesis 1:2 states "And the Spirit of God was hovering over the face of the waters."

CREATION TEXTS

The Creation of the World

> "In the beginning, God created the heavens and the earth.
> The earth was without form and void, and darkness was
> over the face of the deep. And the Spirit of God
> was hovering over the face of the waters."
> *Genesis 1:1-2 ESV*

The Logos

> "In the beginning was the Word and the Word was with God,
> and the Word was God. He was in the beginning with God.
> All things were made through him, and without him
> was not any thing made that was made."
> *John 1:1-3 ESV*

God Spoke

> "By the Word of the LORD the heavens were made,
> and by the breath of his mouth all their host."
> *Psalm 33:6 ESV*

Formed Earth To Be Inhabited

"For thus says the LORD, who created the heavens (he is God!),
who formed the earth and made it (he established it;
he did not create it empty, he formed it to be inhabited!);
I am the LORD, and there is no other."
Isaiah 45:18 ESV

By Faith

"By faith we understand that the universe was created
by the word of God, so that what is seen was
not made out of things that are visible."
Hebrews 11:3 ESV

Upholds the Universe

"He is the radiance of the glory of God and the exact imprint of
his nature, and he upholds the universe by the word of his power."
Hebrews 1:3 ESV

Creator and Sustainer

"All things were created through him and for him.
And he is before all things, and in him all things hold together."
Colossians 1:16b-17 ESV

The Expanse

"And God said "Let there be an expanse in the midst of the
waters, and let it separate the waters from the waters." And God
made the expanse and separated the waters that were under
the expanse from the waters that were above the expanse. And
it was so. And God called the expanse Heaven. And there was
evening and there was morning, the second day."

Genesis 1:6-8 ESV

Waters Above

"Praise him, you highest heavens,
and you waters above the heavens!"
Psalm 148:4 ESV

The Most High

"The sentence is by the decree of the watchers, the decision by
the word of the holy ones, to the end that the living may know
that the Most High rules the kingdom of men and gives it to
whom he will and sets over it the lowliest of men."
Daniel 4:17 ESV

Craftsmanship On Display

"The heavens proclaim the glory of God.
The skies display his craftsmanship."
Psalm 19:1-6 NLT

Let Everything Praise the Lord

"Praise the Lord!
Praise God in his sanctuary;
praise him in his mighty heavens!"
Psalm 50:1 ESV

His Vault

"Who builds his upper chambers in the heavens and founds his vault upon the earth; who calls for the waters of the sea and pours them out upon the surface of the earth—the Lord is his name."
Amos 9:6 ESV

Awe-Inspiring Crystal

"Over the heads of the living creatures there was the likeness of an expanse, shining like awe-inspiring crystal, spread out above their heads."
Ezekiel 1:22 ESV

Like A Throne

"Then I looked, and behold, on the expanse that was over the heads of the cherubim there appeared above them something like a sapphire, in appearance like a throne."
Ezekiel 10:1 ESV

Cast Metal Mirror

"Can you, like him, spread out the skies, hard as a cast metal mirror?"
Job 37:18 ESV

Sits Above the Circle

"It is he who sits above the circle of the earth, and its inhabitants are like grasshoppers; who stretches out the heavens like a curtain."
Isaiah 40:22 ESV

Walks on the Vault

> "Thick clouds veil him, so that he does not see,
> and he walks on the vault of heaven."
> *Job 22:14 ESV*

The Sky

> "The sky vanished like a scroll that is being rolled up, and every
> mountain and island was removed from its place."
> *Revelation 6:14 ESV*

Strong's Concordance # 7549

Strong's # 7549. raqia: an extended surface, expanse. Noun masculine. Phonetic Spelling: raw-kee'-ah.

From raqa. Definition: an extended surface, expanse. Expanse: used 16 times in Genesis. Expanse of heaven: used one time in Genesis.

Brown-Driver-Briggs

Noun masculine. Genesis 1:6 extended surface, (solid) expanse (as if beaten out; compare Job 37:18).

The vault of heaven, or 'firmament,' regarded by Hebrews as solid, and supporting 'waters' above it, Genesis 1:6,7 (used three times in verses).

FIRM-A-MENT

The firm-a-ment is a solid structure. It's firm. Solid hardened glass. The firmament or expanse describes the sky in terms of how it appears from the Earth. The Hebrew suggests something flat and hard, beaten out. Job 37:18 says God spread out the skies, hard as a cast metal mirror. The firmament is made of hardened glass. Isaiah 40:22 says God sits on the circle of the earth, and its inhabitants (people) are like grasshoppers (small). It's a matter of God's perspective. God stretched out the heavens like a curtain and spreads them like a tent to dwell in. A tent is always set up on flat ground, not on a curved place or hill. The sky or expanse is a glass dome that covers the whole earth. The expanse is not space or outer space. You can't beat out space. The sun, moon, and stars are all suspended under the dome. They rotate east to west. The stars are not embedded into the sky. The dome does not turn. It sets on the earth beyond the 200 feet high ice wall. The earth is fixed.

The terms vault, expanse, dome, sky, heaven and the firmament all refer to the same thing. The third heaven is where God dwells. In 2 Corinthians 12:2, the Apostle Paul said he knew a man who was caught up to the third heaven - into paradise - the dwelling place of God. God sits on top of the dome, which is over the earth. God is not that far away. He dwells on the other side of the sky. Our benevolent God, who is sovereign, brought order to earth in the interests of human life and security. Our Father in the heavens wants His will to be done on earth as it is in the third heaven.

"The earth is the LORD'S and the fullness thereof, the world and
those who dwell therein, for he has founded it upon the seas
and established it upon the rivers."
Psalm 24:1-2 ESV

Nevada Desert

Wikileaks released cut scenes of the moon landing filmed in a Nevada desert confirming that the Americans have not been on the Moon. This video proves the moon landing was a hoax. It casts a dark shadow on the entire Apollo Space Program.

What was NASA's intention? Deception. NASA's motive? Pride. The U.S. Federal Government wanted to be known for putting the first man on the Moon, even if it meant faking the whole event, which they did.

July 20, 2019 was the 50th anniversary of the first Moon landing [HOAX] that took place on July 20, 1969. The publication of the video is revenge for the arrest of Julian Assange by the UK authorities on Washington's orders. Julian Assange is Donald Trump's brother's son.

Look up: APOLLOgate.

The Moon Landing Was Completely Fake

Did Apollo 11 land on the Moon on July 20, 1969 ? No. Was Neil Armstrong the first man to walk on the Moon? He never did. But it was on TV. Astronauts are paid actors. Some of the astronauts are Christians, but they lied to the public. Big money to play act. NASA faked the Moon landing. Hollywood went to the Moon on a sound stage in black and white. It was the greatest hoax of them all. You can't land on a light. The Moon is the lesser light. The Sun is the greater light. The same Hebrew word for light is used for both the sun and the moon. Both are luminaries. Sunlight and Moonbeam. Sun rays and rays of the Moon. The sun and the moon are about the same size (34 miles wide) and are about the same distance from earth (3,100 miles). There is no sunlit portion of the moon. The Moon is a disc, not a spherical ball. The lunar phase gradually rotates which turns the face of the moon at an angle or out-of-phase as viewed from earth. A full Moon faces 100% directly toward the earth. Neither the earth's shadow nor the sun's orbit have anything to do with the phases of the moon. Moonbeam is its own light. Is there a Moon River? Only in a song. Is it wider than a mile? Maybe. There is no water on the Moon. The Man in the Moon said so. Sometimes you can see through it with visible clouds on the backside. Why is the sky black with no stars in the photos taken on the Moon? Who took the photo of Apollo 11 lifting off the Moon? Did they go back for him?

The Magnetic Earth

The Earth is surrounded by a magnetic belt, which helps man in navigation and it acts as a powerful invisible shield against solar radiation. The magnetic belt acts as an invisible shield against solar wind, which carries deadly, electrically-charged particles.

The Van Allen Radiation Belt

The Van-Allen radiation shield is unique to earth. In the beginning God created the presence of the Earth's large and heavy metallic core as a radiation shield. Surrounding the Earth in the outer atmosphere are two doughnut-shaped zones known as the Van Allen Radiation Belt, which act as invisible shields against radiation from the sun and outer space. The belts are trapped in the Earth's magnetic field. The "Van-Allen Belt" is unique to earth. ("The Van Allen Belt" was discovered in 1958 by James Van Allen of the University of Iowa.)

Earth has the highest density of any of the planets in our Solar System. This large nickel-iron core is responsible for our large magnetic field. This magnetic field produces the Van-Allen radiation shield, which protects the Earth from radiation bombardment. If this shield were not present, life would not be possible on the Earth. The only other rocky planet to have any magnetic field is Mercury - but its field strength is 100 times less than the Earth's. Even Venus, our sister planet, has no magnetic field.

In 1958, Dr. James Van Allen discovered a collection of high-energy particle clouds within 24,855 miles (40,000 km) of Earth (His estimated distance). Arranged like two nested donuts, the inner belt is mainly energetic protons, while the outer belt contains both protons and electrons. These belts have long been known as 'bad news' for satellites and astronauts, with potentially deadly consequences if you spend too much time within them.

http://www.nuclearplanet.com/

The Van Allen Radiation Belt is a zone of energetic charged particles that are captured and held around a planet by that planet's magnetosphere. Earth has two such belts - the inner Van Allen Belt and the outer radiation belt. These belts are the result of Earth's magnetic field working like a magnetic trap. Can we go through the Van Allen Belt? No. We never went to the moon because of the existence of the Van Allen Radiation Belt. If an astronaut en route to outer space were to pass through these belts, they would receive a lethal dose of radiation. Powerful stuff. With today's technology, NASA still has the inability to penetrate the harsh radiation of the Van Allen Belts.

Uniformitarianism

Uniformitarianism is an evolutionary theory. This view claims that the rate at which an event happens in the present is the same as it was in the past. In other words, the way things are now are the way they have always been. Uniformitarianism: the past is the key to the present. No, the Bible is the key to the past. The debate between uniformitarianism, an evolutionary concept, and a worldwide catastrophic flood is addressed in 2 Peter 3:3-6. Creationists believe that the Bible is true and the Flood of Noah happened just the way it said it did.

Uniformitarianism holds that changes in the earth's crust during geological history (billions of years) have resulted from the action of continuous and uniform processes. The modern view of uniformitarianism incorporates both rates (past and present) of geological processes.

The magnetic field was much stronger prior to the Flood. There was a much higher concentration of ozone under the canopy prior to the Flood. Radiometric dating methods are seriously inaccurate. The entire system of uniformitarianism hinges on the basis that today's environment is exactly like it was billions of years ago. This is ludicrous and silly. Radiometric dating techniques - upon which evolutionists rely to confirm their theory of an old Earth - would definitely be altered if the canopy, the ozone layer and the magnetic field were considered.

"Knowing this first of all, that scoffers will come in the last days with scoffing, following their own sinful desires. They will say, "Where is the promise of his coming? For ever since the fathers fell asleep, all things are continuing as they were from the beginning of creation." For they deliberately overlook this fact, that the heavens existed long ago, and the earth was formed out of water and through water by the word of God, and that by means of these the world that then existed was deluged with water and perished."
2 Peter 3:3-6 ESV

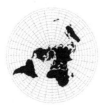

THE FLAT EARTH MOVEMENT

Dr. Kent Hovind of Creation Science Evangelism Ministries and Dinosaur Adventure Land in Repton, AL, is a King James Version only translation of the Bible fundamentalist. Known as Dr. Dino, he claims that the Flat Earth Movement was reintroduced in 2012. Dr. Dino says this movement was reintroduced to divide Christians and discredit the Bible. The atheists or evolutionists are behind it, and the devil is laughing at us. He says this movement is distracting Christians from fulfilling the Great Commission. He says its dumb because flat-earthers give Redneck answers. He says it's causing Christians to fight one another and to disagree and debate on this issue. Dr. Kent Hovind believes and promotes the heliocentric model and the ball earth model. Kent repeats over and over again that the earth is not flat, and he repeats over and over again that the earth is a global ball spinning at 1,038 mph at the equator. Kent says that the Bible does not teach the earth is flat or unmovable. He believes the earth is spinning at 1,038 mph at the equator but there is zero spin at the North Pole. He says suppose a missile is shot at a target 20 minutes away, it would miss the target if the rotation of the earth was not programmed into the mathematical calculation to give you the lead distance. He claims we get the Gulf Stream currents from the spinning earth. No, the Gulf Stream is caused by a large system of circular currents and powerful winds. He says that the stars are embedded in the sky and don't rotate. We get the circle of stars at night in open lens photos from the spinning of the earth. The stars don't move, but the earth does. He says gravity is the attraction of the masses. Gravity is inside the earth and attracts objects to the surface. Brother Hovind believes that the earth can orbit the sun everyday in the solar system and still be the center of God's attention. Instead of quoting any of the 67 verses in the Bible that say the earth does not move, he quoted several verses completely out of context which, he says, say that the earth moves. He misinterpreted and misapplied six verses. Here are his examples: Psalm 18:7 says the earth reeled and rocked; the foundations also of the mountains trembled and quaked. Why? Because God was angry. This verse is about God's judgment. It's not talking about a moving earth. 2 Samuel 22:8 says the same thing, the earth shook because God was angry. Psalm 99:1 says, "let the earth quake" because the LORD reigns; let the peoples tremble! No moving earth going on here. Jeremiah 50:46 says "At the sound of the capture of Babylon the earth shall tremble, and her cry shall be heard among the nations." He said, "See, the earth trembles. The earth moves." Jeremiah Chapters 50 and 51 are talking about the utter judgment on Babylon, not a moving earth. Isaiah 24 focuses on God's overthrow of the corrupted earth. Sounds like judgment on the wickedness of man in the days of Noah. No moving earth going on here either. Isaiah 24:1-27:13 is about judgment of the whole earth.

Ladies and gentlemen. This is a prime time example of exegesis. Kent Hovind read his own ideas into these texts.

It's a Mad, Mad, Mad, Mad World starring Nick Copernicus and the Orbits. The Orbits are Nick's backup group. All their fans sing the same heliocentric tune as they follow the spinning ball.

Christian Creationists who believe the earth orbits the sun and believe the earth is a round ball seem to have the attitude that Christian Creationists who believe in a non-moving earth and that the earth is a flat plane do not have the right to debate and defend their views. A good education allows for a level playing field where all ideas are heard equally. This debate and discussion should be between Christian Creationists who hold different views, not between Christian Creationists and secular scientists who are wrong about everything having to do with scientific matters.

Up until the Scopes Trial in Dayton, TN in 1925, all public schools taught the Genesis account of creation. All of our Founding Fathers were creationists.

Thomas Jefferson wrote: ...all men are created equal, that they are endowed by their Creator...

After the Scopes Monkey Trial, Darwinian evolution began to be taught along side of biblical creation. In time, the secular scientists pushed biblical creation out of the classroom and allowed only Darwinian evolution to be taught. Their reasoning was evolution is science and creation is religion. Genesis is literal history that is inspired. Creationism is not a religion. In fact, evolution is a religion. It takes more faith to believe that once upon a time, far, far away there was nothing, and it exploded, than it does to believe: "In the beginning God created the heavens and the earth."

Students are now being indoctrinated that they evolved from lower life forms, not educated that they are created in the image of God. Imago Dei.

The heliocentric adherents are doing the same thing to geocentric adherents that the evolutionists did to the Creationists after the Scopes Trial. They are trying to exclude them from the debate and make fun of their ideas.

Until his death in 2001, Charles Johnson of Lancaster, California was the head of the International Flat Earth Research Society, an organization with a claimed membership of 3,500. The members of his society were very serious about their contention that the shape of Earth is flat rather than spherical. To flat-earthers many passages in the Bible say that God created an Earth that is shaped like a coin, not a ball: flat and round at the edges. Good theology requires the Bible to be read as literally true. The Englishman responsible for the 19th century revival of the flat Earth model, Samuel Rowbotham, cited 67 scripture verses that say the earth does not move. For flat-earthers the Bible takes first place over the information provided by secular science. Secular science information changes, the scriptures do not. Most cosmology and astronomy textbooks are out of date. These secular scientists are to be held in error.

The 1985 National Creation Conference in Cleveland, Ohio ended with a formal debate on the relative merits of heliocentricity and geocentricity. The issues were debated.

From their geographical and historical context, one would expect the ancient Hebrews of the OT to have a flat-earth cosmology. From the beginning, ultra-orthodox Christians have been flat-earthers, arguing that to believe otherwise is to deny the literal truth of the Bible. The flat-earth implications of the Bible were rediscovered and popularized by English-speaking Christians in the mid-19th century. Liberal scriptural scholars later derived the same view. College students with disparate points of view independently concluded that the ancient Hebrews had a flat-earth cosmology, often deriving this view from scripture alone.

The Council of Jerusalem

The Jerusalem Council was a conference of the apostles in Jerusalem around AD 50. James, the half-brother of Jesus, was the pastor of the church in Jerusalem. They decreed that Gentile Christians did not have to observe the Mosaic Law of the Jews. Paul and Barnabas had no small dissension and debate with the men from Judea. Paul acknowledged that forcing Gentiles to be circumcised would make them think that salvation must be earned. He knew that the Judaizers had to be opposed because they would hinder the extension of the gospel to the Gentiles.

Since the early church, Christians have disagreed and debated important doctrinal issues. There is nothing wrong with Christians having a debate to resolve their differences on important issues. Debates are valuable activities for students. Good debaters learn to explain their own ideas and evaluate different viewpoints. A debate is a formal discussion on a particular topic in a public meeting in which opposing arguments are put forward. Christian Creationists can disagree, but they should disagree agreeably. Debaters should not call flat-earthers names and say their answers are red neck when they are quoting the Bible. Christian Creationists who believe and defend the geocentric model and the flat-earth model are sincere and support their views based on the Bible. They have no ulterior motive. The Bible says 67 times that the earth does move. They believe that.

The Michelson-Morley experiment proved scientifically that the earth does not move. Gleason's NEW STANDARD MAP OF THE WORLD is scientifically and practically correct; as "it is." This map is a visual illustration of what the flat-earth looks like with the North Pole in the center.

Water seeks it own level. Water does not seek a perpendicular position on a round globe spinning at 1,038 mph. Gravity in the earth does not attract the quintillion gallons of water in the seas while earth is spinning at 1,038 mph tilted on an axis sideways. Water in the oceans is at sea level from shore to shore. Water in the oceans does not curve or raise eight inches at one mile's distance. Yes, dry land has mountain ranges, cliffs, hills, valleys, ravines, gorges, and canyons, but it is a flat-plane with rough topography in places, not a round globe. Topography is the study of the landforms and features of land surfaces. Most surface landforms of the earth are the result of the catastrophic Flood of Noah approximately 4,359 years ago or 2348 BC.

Kansas is flat. Texas is flat. Nebraska is flat. The Bonneville Salt Flats in northwestern Utah is the largest of many salt flats located west of the Great Salt Lake. Railroads are flat. Bridges are flat. Seas are flat. Rivers are flat. Highways are flat. Race tracks are flat. Building foundations are flat. A flat is a single story housing unit. All vertical planes with no curves, no bends, no horizon dips, no apparent horizon dips without atmospheric refraction.

The flat-earth cosmology is historically consistent and requires none of the special imploring apparently necessary to harmonize the Bible with sphericity.

Answers In Genesis

Answers in Genesis is an apologetics ministry, dedicated to helping Christians defend their faith and proclaim the good news of Jesus Christ effectively. It focuses on providing answers to questions about the Bible - particularly the Book of Genesis - regarding key issues such as creation, evolution, science, and the age of the earth.

Answer in Genesis built two top notch tourist attractions in northern Kentucky. The Creation Museum in Petersburg, KY, and the Ark Encounter in Williamstown, KY. Bible history comes to life at the Creation Museum! A family-friendly attraction explores creation science with exhibits, dinosaur bones, fossils, botanical gardens, a planetarium, zoo, zip line course, and more. The Ark Encounter features a full-size Noah's ark. It's huge. Three stories high with three levels of exhibits. It's 510 feet long, 85 feet wide, and 51 feet high. The ark had the same storage capacity as about 450 standard semi-trailers. Both are worth visiting.

Falling Flat

In his book, Falling Flat, Dr. Danny R. Faulkner of Answers in Genesis writes that flat earth fallacies are just one more way to muddy the waters in the creation and evolution debate, as well as trying to discredit the Bible as being inaccurate and Christianity as an empty hoax. He claims that the flat-earth model is a fallacy filled with untruths and misleading agendas. His book claims to give powerful answers to refute misleading and false flat earth claims.

He says his book gives important, thoroughly researched, historical and scientific evidences disproving a flat earth, and vital context of biblical truths and effective apologetics for Christians.

Faulkner further says his book gives a fascinating look at discoveries, science, and the Church throughout history as it faces down and disproves over and over again flat earth fallacies.

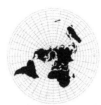

FLAT EARTH DEBUNKED

In a taped seminar at the Creation Museum, Danny Faulkner, a creationist astronomer with Answer in Genesis, attempts to debunk the flat-earth model. Faulkner is a vocal opponent of what he calls biblical, enclosed cosmology (flat-earth). He claims the flat-earth model is a conspiracy. He associated it with Gnosticism, which is a heresy. Gnosticism is the belief that learning secret knowledge brings salvation or at the very least leads to spiritual enlightenment. The Apostle John and the Apostle Paul both wrote against Gnostic philosophy.

Faulkner set out to answer the question: Is the Earth Flat? He seemed disturbed that there is a resurgent flat-earth movement. He said he feels that the flat-earth model is a personal assault on his calling and Answers in Genesis. In an Answers TV broadcast, Danny Faulkner joined with Dr. Georgia Purdom, a molecule geneticist at Answers in Genesis, to debunk the flat-earth model. They both laughed and made light of the verses flat-earthers use to support their view. Dr. Purdom agreed with everything Faulkner said.

What Faulkner Believes

Unbelievably, here is what he believes: That the dome contains the stars. The dome turns each day, producing the motion of stars that we see each night. That the Bedford level experiment conducted by Rowbatham 180 years ago showed that in one mile distance of a six mile canal the view of the ship with a flag on it was blocked by the curvature of the earth, that Rowbatham ignored atmospheric refraction caused by temperature inversions, that those who hold to the flat earth view believe creation equals a flat earth, that the Heliocentric model is true, that the earth goes around the sun, that the sun rising and setting is not perspective, that the earth spins on its axis, that the Bible does not say the earth is flat, that the moon is a reflection of the sun, that the sun is 93 million miles above the earth, not 3,100 miles away from earth and not 34 miles wide, that he can prove the earth is a globe from a photo he took of a lunar eclipse that shows the circle of earth's shadow, that lunar eclipses are caused by the earth's shadow, that the dome looks like a dome but it is not a dome, the dome is an illusion, the sky spins around, that the firmament is not the sky, that the Hebrew word raqis in Genesis 1:9 does not mean the solid vault of heaven, the dome looks like a dome at night, but that doesn't mean it is a dome, that the dome contains the stars and turns each day producing the motion of stars that we see each night, that the stars themselves don't move, that the dome is a myth, that the flat earth myth came from 19th century archaeological "cosmology" of the Ancient Near East (ANE), that the expanse is not the firmament, that the flat-earthers believe the dome is like a snow globe with no glitter, that the North Star (Polaris) is not visible from the southern hemisphere, that the earth is spherical, that the curvature of the earth blocks the view of a ship off in a distance because water bends eight inches per mile, that you can't zoom in to see the hull of a ship because it disappears below the curvature of the water, that a picture of the Chicago skyline taken from the southern shore of Michigan almost 60 miles away is a mirage, an optical phenomenon, that Greek Eratosthenes circa 200 BC measured earth's circumference at 25,000 miles around, that flat-earthers use exegesis (Greek: reading into a text one's own ideas) to interpret Isaiah 40:22, that God 'sits enthroned above the circle of the earth', that this is not the dome and does not mean heaven is above the firmament, that the South Pole exists, that the phrase "the four corners of the earth" in Isaiah 11:12 and Revelation 7:1 means NESW = four cardinal directions, the "ends of the earth" in Psalm 76:7 is talking about people, not directions, that the enormously tall tree in Daniel 4:10-18 was a dream of King Nebuchadnezzar, a pagan king, and dreams are not real; he laughed and mocked the dream King Nebuchadnezzar had and said it was no different than his own unusual dreams, that God does not use dreams to speak messages to men, that the tree did not touch the sky and was not visible to the ends of the earth; that this is not teaching cosmology, he did not mention that God often used dreams in the Bible to communicate to people, e.g., in Joel 2:28 your old men will dream dreams, in Acts 2:17 old men will dream dreams, in Genesis 37:1-44:9 Joseph had a dream, in Daniel 1:17 Daniel could understand dreams of all kinds, in Genesis 20:3 God came to Abimelek in a dream, in Matthew 1:20-23 an angel of the Lord appeared to Joseph in a dream, in Matthew 2:13 an angel of the Lord appeared to Joseph in a dream, in Matthew 2:19 an angel of the Lord appeared in a dream to Joseph in Egypt, in Numbers 12:6 'I speak to them in dreams,' in Daniel 7:1-3 Daniel had a dream, in Deuteronomy 13:1-3 one who foretells by dreams, in Genesis 41:8-12 each of us had a dream, in Job 33:14-18 for God does speak in a dream, and in Genesis 28:10-17 Jacob dreamed of angels ascending and descending, that Daniel's dream in his bed in Daniel 4:10-18 was about a pagan king not a tall tree touching the sky, that the rim along the outer edge of the flat earth is not a 200 feet high 'Ice Wall' on the coast of Antarctica and is vital for the climate. That the flat-earth movement threatens to marginalize the church and ultimately undermine the reliability of Scripture. That the motivation of flat-earthers is to present a prank, to be malicious, to mock Christianity and make it look bad. He accuses flat-earthers of making false accusations, he accuses them of a total misapplication of scripture, accuses them of scripture twisting, he accused them of pride for claiming to know something about the flat-earth model with no science education or degrees.

God's Word, the Authority!

Ken Ham is the CEO and founder of Answers in Genesis-US, the Creation Museum, and the Ark Encounter.

Ken Ham says, "How can we teach them? Well, we must show them that God's Word is the authority. It's the infallible, inspired Word from our Creator."

Answers in Genesis holds the correct biblical view on creation science in Genesis, Adam and Eve, man created in the image of God, fall of man, sin and salvation, skin color, only two genders, marriage, family, age of the earth, Noah's ark, the Flood of Noah, dinosaurs and dinosaur bones, and fossils. But their views, like other Christian creationists, are against the geocentric model and the flat-earth model. They hold to a non-biblical and non-scientific view of astronomy and cosmology.

They are as wrong on these two subjects as they are right on all the other subjects. They couldn't be anymore wrong. Why do they or anyone hold distorted views of realities? Because they have been indoctrinated with Darwinian evolution and they don't even recognize it. They have been deceived by the fathers of lies. Indoctrination is a process of training a person or group to accept a set of beliefs uncritically.

Will Ken Ham, Danny Faulkner and the Answers in Genesis ministry change their view on the Heliocentric model and the global ball model? Probably not. Why not? Two basic reasons: (1) they think their views on astronomy and cosmology are right, and (2) they would not want to deal with all the public criticism and negative feedback from the secular science community and from Christian colleges and universities that teach the heliocentric model and global ball model in their courses.

A high percentage of Christian colleges and universities teach the heliocentric model and global ball model in their astronomy and cosmology courses. Also, AiG would not want to deal with all the fundamentalists and evangelical pastors who hold the same views, and teach and preach it in their churches.

AiG has chosen to believe pseudoscience instead of the truth of Scripture. AiG has denied and/or ignored what the Word of God clearly teaches regarding the geocentric model and the flat-earth model. Obviously, Danny Faulkner does not have a high view of the Bible. He sarcastically makes light of the clear biblical texts that support the geocentric model and the flat-earth model. Some texts he totally ignores. He failed to mention any of the 67 verses that say the earth does not move.

Christian creationists, pastors and professors, have an unjustifiable (and incoherent) position of claiming that they're being scientifically-minded in accepting the spherical earth model and the solar system with a non-moving sun - but they insist that their so-called creation science justifies their creationism. So we should have no problem criticizing them for promoting their pseudoscience and also for denying their scriptural inconsistency.

Don't forget, Galileo was arrested, tried and convicted of heresy for his arguments for Copernicanism or heliocentrism. The charge of heresy is a serious charge. Heresy is a belief contrary to orthodox Christian doctrine. He was placed under house arrest for the rest of his life. The church was right then and is still right. Galileo was flat wrong then, and he's still wrong.

It's rather difficult to respect the staff of any Christian organization or pastor of a local church who hold a belief contrary to the clear-cut teachings in the Bible regarding the non-moving earth and the shape of the earth being a flat plane. God so loved the world, not the sun. We do not live in a solar system, we live in a geocentric system. God's green earth is fixed. The earth is the central focus of the universe. God worked six days to make earth habitable for man. He spent one day to create the sun, moon, and stars or planets. God's world is geocentric, not heliocentric. Geocentrism is proved from the Bible, and supported by true science. Likewise, the flat-earth is proved from the Bible, and supported by true science. It's not flat-earth vs. science. Flat-earth is not a theory. Flat-earth is not a conspiracy or a plot. Flat-earth is not a myth or a metaphor. Flat-earth is not a joke or an idiomatic expression. Flat-earth is not a cult. Flat-earth is literal, not figurative. There is no such thing as a flat-earth gospel. The Gospel is the good news of Jesus Christ.

Flat-earth is part of biblical cosmology. Cosmology is the science of the origin and development of the cosmos. Modern astronomy is dominated by the Big Bang theory, which is an unproven theory, not a model. Modern astronomy needs to be dominated by Creation science, the geocentric model, and the flat-earth model. Modern astronomy should not be dominated by the Big Bang theory, which is Darwinian evolution, and not dominated by the heliocentric model, which is Copernicanism, and not dominated by the global spherical model, which was an invention of Martin Behaim in German in 1492. Before this German cartographer all world maps were flat.

Be Careful What You Believe

If you don't believe the Earth is flat, stationary, and in the center of the universe, then you have been indoctrinated with the view of pseudoscientific Darwinian evolution.

If you believe God created the cosmos and all that exists ex nihilo (out of nothing) instead of ex logos (out of the spoken Word), then you have been indoctrinated with the view of pseudoscientific Darwinian evolution.

If you believe the Bible teaches Theistic evolution, then you have caved to the view of pseudoscientific Darwinian evolution.

If you believe the Bible teaches Darwinian evolution, then you have been indoctrinated with the view of pseudoscientific Darwinian evolution.

If you do not believe the Bible is a geocentric book from Genesis to maps, then you have been indoctrinated with the view of pseudoscientific Darwinian evolution.

If you believe the theory of Darwinian evolution is true in any form and deny the Genesis account of Creation, then you have been indoctrinated with the view of pseudoscientific Darwinian evolution.

If you believe there is more than one race of humans, then you have been indoctrinated with the view of pseudoscientific Darwinian evolution.

If you do not believe all human beings are made from "one blood" (one man, Adam), then you have been indoctrinated with the view of pseudoscientific Darwinian evolution.

If you believe there are more than two genders (male and female), then you have been indoctrinated with the view of pseudoscientific Darwinian evolution.

If you believe God created human beings with red, yellow, black, and white skin color, then you have been indoctrinated with the view of pseudoscientific Darwinian evolution.

If you do not believe God created one race, (human race) and one skin color (brown), then you have been indoctrinated with the view of pseudoscientific Darwinian evolution.

If you do not believe that the amount of melanin pigment inherited from your parents determines your skin tone, then you have been indoctrinated with the view of pseudoscientific Darwinian evolution.

If you believe the Heliocentric model and deny the Geocentric model, then you have been indoctrinated with the view of pseudoscientific Darwinian evolution.

If you believe the earth is a round globe spinning at 1,038 mph tilted on an axis, then you have been indoctrinated with the view of pseudoscientific Darwinian evolution.

If you believe the earth is not fixed, then you have been indoctrinated with the view of pseudoscientific Darwinian evolution.

If you believe the earth moves, then you have been indoctrinated with the view of pseudoscientific Darwinian evolution.

If you believe the earth goes around the sun, then you have been indoctrinated with the view of pseudoscientific Darwinian evolution.

If you believe the sun does not move, then you have been indoctrinated with the view of pseudoscientific Darwinian evolution.

If you believe the sun is the center of the solar system, then you have been indoctrinated with the view of pseudoscientific Darwinian evolution.

If you believe the sun is 93 million miles away from earth, then you have been indoctrinated with the view of pseudoscientific Darwinian evolution.

If you believe the earth is spinning on an axis at 1,038 mph, then you have been indoctrinated with the view of pseudoscientific Darwinian evolution.

If you believe the earth is rotating around the sun at 67,000 mph, then you have been indoctrinated with the view of pseudoscientific Darwinian evolution.

If you believe the moon's light is a reflection of the sun, then you have been indoctrinated with the view of pseudoscientific Darwinian evolution.

If you do not believe both the Sun and the Moon are luminaries (lights), then you have been indoctrinated with the view of pseudoscientific Darwinian evolution.

If you do not believe the 67 verses in the Bible that say the earth does not move, then you are ignorant of what the Bible says.

If you believe the Copernican Revolution was right, then you have been indoctrinated with the view of pseudoscientific Darwinian evolution.

If you believe Galileo was right and the church was wrong in the 1633, then you have been indoctrinated with the view of pseudoscientific Darwinian evolution.

If you do not believe earth is suspended in space by electromagnetic power between the North Pole and Polaris, then you have been indoctrinated with the view of pseudoscientific Darwinian evolution.

If you believe the global Earth model has an axial tilt of 24.4° off of true North, then you have been indoctrinated with the view of pseudoscientific Darwinian evolution.

If you do not believe God created earth vertical, then you have been indoctrinated with the view of pseudoscientific Darwinian evolution.

If you believe earth's polar axis is at a 66.6° angle, then you have been indoctrinated with the view of pseudoscientific Darwinian evolution.

If you believe there is a rotation axis of the earth, then you have been indoctrinated with the view of pseudoscientific Darwinian evolution.

If you do not believe the North celestial pole is due North, and is instead tilted on an axis, then you have been indoctrinated with the view of pseudoscientific Darwinian evolution.

If you do not believe God actually stopped the sun and the moon in the sky for Joshua (Joshua 10:13), then you have been indoctrinated with the view of pseudoscientific Darwinian evolution.

If you believe the stopping of the sun and the moon in the sky was apparent (Joshua 10:13), then you have been indoctrinated with the view of pseudoscientific Darwinian evolution.

If you do not believe the earth is a flat plane, without orbital or axial motion, then you have been indoctrinated with the view of pseudoscientific Darwinian evolution.

If you do not believe "sea level" means the oceans are level all over the earth, then you have been indoctrinated with the view of pseudoscientific Darwinian evolution.

If you believe the moon affects the ebb and flow of tides, then you have been indoctrinated with the view of pseudoscientific Darwinian evolution.

If you have a blue ocean world globe model with a tilted axis rotation in your home, church, school, library, business, or office, then you are worshiping an idol and are promoting a false representation of God's geocentric creation and have been indoctrinated with the view of pseudoscientific Darwinian evolution.

Incompatible Models

Truth about reality is knowable. There is truth to be known. Objective truth is knowable. The opposite of true is false. The Geocentric Model is knowable. The Flat Earth Model is knowable.

The Geocentric Model and the Heliocentric Model are diametrical opposites. One is true, and one is false. The two models are incompatible. They are so opposed in evidence and support as to be incapable of existing together. The Heliocentric Model is junk science. It is as phony as a three dollar bill. A three dollar bill is counterfeit currency. It has no value. You can't spend it. The problem is this: since the Copernican Revolution began in 1543, the year of his death, the heliocentric nonsensical model advocates has been printing and distributing their phony three dollar bills all over the world. Heliocentric followers think three dollar bills have value because that's what they've been told over and over again. But they are phony. Fake. Worthless. Don't invest your time and money in something that is not supported by Scripture and not backed by true scientific evidence. Mark Twain said, "It's easier to fool people than to convince them that they have been fooled." If you were indoctrinated once, it will take years to get over it.

Remember, evolution is not science. It's a humanistic religion masked as pseudoscience. It's a big lie. Heliocentric ideology is not science. It's fabricated pseudoscience. The global ball earth theory is not science. It too is fabricated pseudoscience. All three of these theories are as phony as a three dollar bill. They are all masquerading as gold / asset-backed currency, when in actuality, they are all worthless fiat paper currencies. All three theories are bankrupt. They have no intrinsic value.

Has your mind been programmed with pseudoscience? Have you been fooled? Have you been tricked? Have you been lied to? Have you been indoctrinated and don't know it? Everything cannot be true. Take the time to think things through. Question the Darwinian evolutionary theory. Doubt Darwin. Question the Heliocentric Nonsensical Model. Question the Global Ball Earth theory. Are you open-minded enough to study the Genesis record of creation? Are you open-minded enough to study the Geocentric Model? Are you open-minded enough to study the Flat Earth Model?

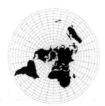

CONCLUSION

This Is My Father's World
Malthie B. Babcock

*This is my Father's world, and to my listening ears all nature sings,
and 'round me rings the music of the spheres.
This is my Father's world: I rest me in the thought of rocks and trees,
of skies and seas—His hand the wonders wrought.
This is my Father's world, The birds their carols raise, the morning light,
the lily white, declare their Maker's praise.
This is my Father's world: He shines in all that's fair, in the rustling grass
I hear Him pass, He speaks to me everywhere.
This is my Father's world, O let me ne'er forget that though the wrong seems
of't so strong, God is the ruler yet.
This is my Father's world, the battle is not done; Jesus who died shall be satisfied,
and earth and heaven be one.
AMEN!*

Non-Moving Earth
The Best Available Information - Scripture

"He established the earth upon its foundations,
So that it will not totter forever and ever."
Psalm 104:5 NAS

"Tremble before Him, all the earth;
Indeed, the world is firmly established, it will not be moved."
1 Chronicles 16:30

"For He spoke, and it was done; He commanded, and it stood fast."
Psalm 33:9

"The Lord reigns, He is clothed with majesty;
The Lord has clothed and girded Himself with strength;
Indeed, the world is firmly established, it will not be moved."
Psalm 93:1

"Say among the nations, "The Lord reigns;
Indeed, the world is firmly established, it will not be moved;
He will judge the peoples with equity."
Psalm 96:10

"Forever, O Lord, Your word is settled in heaven.
Your faithfulness continues throughout all generations;
You established the earth, and it stands."
Psalm 119:89-90

"The whole earth is at rest and is quiet;
They break forth into shouts of joy."
Isaiah 14:7

"For thus says the Lord, who created the heavens (He is the God
who formed the earth and made it, He established it and did not
create it a waste place, but formed it to be inhabited),
"I am the Lord, and there is none else."
Isaiah 45:18

"So they answered the angel of the Lord who was standing
among the myrtle trees and said, "We have patrolled the earth,
and behold, all the earth is peaceful and quiet."
Zechariah 1:11

For he was looking for the city which has foundations, whose
architect and builder is God. *(God is both the architect (designer,
blueprints) and the builder (Trinity Construction Company).*
Hebrews 11:10

For when they maintain this, it escapes their notice that
by the word of God the heavens existed long ago
and the earth was formed out of water and by water.
2 Peter 3:5

Fear before him, all the earth: the world also shall be stable,
that it be not moved.
1 Chronicles 16:30

> Who laid the foundations of the earth,
> that it should not be removed for ever.
> *Psalm 104:5*

Biblical Evidence

In Galileo's heresy trial, two Bible verses were used, which indicate that the sun orbits the earth:

> "The sun arises, and the sun goes down,
> and hastens to the place where he rises."
> *Ecclesiastes 1:5 ESV*

> "Sun, stand still at Gibeon, and moon, in the valley of Aijalon."
> And the sun stood still, and the moon stopped,
> until the nation took vengeance on their enemies.
> *Joshua 10:12-13*

> Is this not written in the Book of Jasher? The sun stopped in the midst of heaven, and did not hurry to set for about a whole day."
> *Joshua 10:13 ESV*

NOTE: Anybody or any institution that teaches the heliocentric model as fact is as guilty as Galileo was then and for the same thing.

How Then Should We Live Now?

We should live in the reality that in the beginning, around 6,000 years ago, Elohim created everything that exists—time, energy, space and matter. God created mankind in His own image and likeness, and we are guests on God's green fixed and flat earth that is in the center of the cosmos. That man's chief end is to glorify God and enjoy Him forever. We enter His gates with thanksgiving and His courts with praise.

APPENDIX

Appendix I

The Flat Earth Guy

Dave Weiss, known as "Dave, the flat earth guy," created the Flat Earth Sun, Moon & Zodiac app for $2.99. The app has 21 features of research. The Flat Earth Clock is provided by Blue Water Bay. Dave is host of the Dave Weiss podcast. Visit: TheFlatEarthPodcast.com. Deep Inside the Rabbit Hole (DITRH) aka Dave Weiss features short videos on YouTube. The Flat Earth Sun & Moon Clock shows you where you are and where the sun and moon are on their journey around the face of the earth as shown on the Azimuthal Equidistant map. You can see where the daylight and night time are as well as the position and phase of the moon as the sun slowly laps it every month. Track the seasons as the sun travels outward to the Tropic of Capricorn in December and then makes its way inward to the Tropic of Cancer for June.

Appendix II

www.FlatEarth101.com

Appendix III

www.aPlaneTruth.info

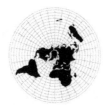

BIBLIOGRAPHY

Hank Hanegraaff, *The Creation Answer Book* (Nashville, TN: Thomas Nelson, 2012)

Hank Hanegraaff, *The Complete Bible Answer Book Collector's Edition:* (Nashville, TN, Thomas Nelson, 2008)

Ralph D. Winter & Steven C. Hawthrone, Editors, *Perspectives on the World Christian Movement A Reader Fourth Edition:* (Pasadena, California, William Carey Library, 2009 by the Institute of International Studies)

Steven C. Hawthorne, *Perspectives on the World Christian Movement: The Study Guide Fourth Edition* (Pasadena, CA, William Carey Library, 2009)

Philip Michael Pantana, Sr., *America: A Purpose-Driven Nation One Nation One God One Law:* (Maitland, FL, Xulon Press, 2007)

Dana Sherstad & B.J. Barbich, *Testimony of the Heavens God's Redemptive Plan Preserved in the Stars:* (Woodinville, WA, A Good Name Publishing, 2011)

Marshall Hall, *The Truth About Evolution:* (Cornelia, GA, Bible Based Books, 1974)

Marshall Hall, *The Earth Is Not Moving: 2nd Printing* (Cornelia, GA, Bible Based Books, 1994)

Wayne Grudem, *Politics According To The Bible A Comprehensive Resource for Understanding Modern Political Issues in Light of Scripture:* (Grand Rapids, MI, Zondervan, 2010)

Dennis Prager, *Genesis God, Creation, and Destruction The Rational Bible:* (Washington, DC, Regnery Faith, 2019)

John C. Rankin, *Genesis and the Power of True Assumptions (Second Edition):* (West Simsbury, CT, TEI Publishing House, 2016)

Robert J. Schadewald, *The Flat-Earth Bible:* (Cleveland, OH, Cleveland Publisher, The Bulletin of the Tychonian Society #44, 1987)

Rav Sha'ul, *Creation Cries Out! The Book of the Mazzaroth: 2nd Edition* (Sabbath Covenant, 2015)

Alan F. Johnson & Robert E. Webber, *What Christians Believe A Biblical & Historical Summary:* (Grand Rapids, MI, Zondervan Publishing House, 1993)

Danny Faulkner, *Falling for a Flat Earth Featured in Answers Magazine:* (Petersburg, KY, Answers Magazine, 2018)

Chuck Missler, *Learn the Bible in 24 Hours Genesis Hour 3 Small Groups:* (Post Falls, ID, Koinonia House, 2016)

Gary North, *The Dominion Covenant: Genesis An Economic Commentary on the Bible Volume I* (Tyler, Texas, Institute for Christian Economics, Second Printing, Revised, 1987)

Celebrate Jesus 2000, *What Single Event in Human History Had the Power to Split Time?:* (Alpharetta, GA, Celebrate Jesus 2000, 2000)

Ken Ham, *The Lie Evolution Genesis—The Key to Defending Your Faith:* (Green Forest, AR, Master Books, Inc., Twenty-first printing, 2001)

Hank Hanegraaff, *Has God Spoken? Proof of the Bible's Divine Inspiration:* (Nashville, TN, Thomas Nelson, 2011)

Pastor Tyler J. Doka, YouTube.Com/DokaBaptist, *Flat Earth From a Biblical Perspective: Sermon Part I & Part II* (Long Island, NY, Great Harvest Baptist Church, 2018)

David H. Stern, *Jewish New Testament Commentary:* (Clarksville, MD, Jewish New Testament Publications, Inc., 1992)

F.E. Pasche, *Fifty Reasons Copernicus or the Bible:* (Morris MN, Self-Published, 1915)

Rabbi Jason Sobel, *Mysteries of the Messiah Unveiling Divine Connections from Genesis to Today:* (Nashville, TN, W Publishing Group, an imprint of Thomas Nelson, 2021)

J. Sidlow Baxter, *Explore the Book A Basic and Broadly Interpretative Course of Bible Study from Genesis to Revelation* (Grand Rapids, MI, Zondervan Publishing House, Eighth printing 1970)

Jettie Harris, *God's Opera Finding Truth in Music:* (Forest, VA, Publishers Solution, 2017)

Kenneth L. Gentry, Jr., *God Gave Wine What the Bible Says About Alcohol:* (Lincoln, CA, Oakdown of MenschWerks, 2001)

Robert W. Faid, *A Scientific Approach to Christianity New scientific evidence supports the Bible;* (South Plainfield, NJ, Bridge Publishing, Inc., 1982)

Dennis Gordon Lindsay, *The Canopied Earth: World That War: volume Four* Creation Series (Dallas, TX, Christ For The Nation, Inc., 1991)

John C. Rankin, *Creation and Evolution:* (Hartford, CT, Theological Education Institute, 2007)

Holy Spirit, NET Bible, Full Notes Edition: (Nashville, TN, Thomas Nelson, 2019)

T. Walter Wallbank, Alastair M. Taylor, Nels M. Bailkey, *Civilization Past and Present: Single Volume Third Edition* (Glenview, IL, Scott, Foresman, and Company, 1967)

Donald B. DeYoung, *Weather & the Bible 100 Questions & Answers:* (Grand Rapids, MI, Baker Book House, 1992)

Steve Meyerowitz, *Water The Ultimate Cure:* (Summertown, TN, Book Publishing Company, 2001)

Kevin Craig, http://www.vineandfigtree.org/: (Powersite, MO, Vine & Fig Tree, 2000).

John C. Whitcomb, Jr., *The World That Perished Biblical and Scientific Evidence for the Genesis Flood as a Global Catastrophe:* (Grand Rapids, MI, Baker Book House, 1973)

Ray Comfort, *Scientific Facts in the Bible 100 Reasons to Believe the Bible is Supernatural in Origin:* (Newberry, FL, Bridge-Logos, 2001)

Lee Strobel, *The Case for a Creator A Journalist Investigates Scientific Evidence That Points Toward God:* (Grand Rapids, MI, Zondervan, 2004)

Marvin L. Lubenow, *Bones of Contention A Creationist Assessment of Human Fossils:* Revised and Updated (Grand Rapids, MI, Baker Books, 2004)

Ken Ham, *Creation Evangelism for the New Millennium:* (Green Forest, AR, Master Books, 2000)

Francis A. Schaeffer & C. Everett Koop, M.D., *Whatever Happened to the Human Race? Exposing our rapid yet subtle loss of human rights:* (Old Tappan, NJ, Fleming H. Revell Company, 1979)

Henry Morris, *The Long War Against God: The History and Impact of the Creation/Evolution Conflict:* (Green Forest, AR, Master Books, 2000)

E.W. Bullinger, *The Witness of the Stars:* (Westminster, CA, Alacrity Press, 1893)

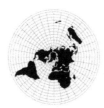

ABOUT THE AUTHOR

Phil Pantana was born on a Wednesday in the month of July in Lima, Ohio, the first born son of Joseph and Alma Pantana. Phil has two brothers, John and David, and a sister, Regina. They grew up in NW Ohio in a farming community where they attended Elida Mennonite School, within walking distance of their home on Bliss Road. The school only went to the eighth grade. The four siblings sang together and made two recordings. Phil then attended Elida Local School in the Village of Elida. After graduating from high school, he attended Moody Bible Institute in Chicago. He graduated from Midwestern Broadcasting School also in Chicago. His educational experiences include: graduating from Bob Jones University in Greenville, SC, Liberty Baptist Theological Seminary in Lynchburg, VA, Southwestern Baptist Theological Seminary in Ft. Worth, TX, and Dallas Theological Seminary in Dallas, TX.

Phil was a member of the faculty of Liberty University in Lynchburg, VA, and taught in the areas of Communications, Music, and Theology. He also started the school Yearbook, Selah, started and programmed the school FM radio station, WRVL, and started the Praise and Worship Studies program with Dr. Robert Webber from Wheaton College in IL, and Northern Baptist Theological Seminary in Lisle, IL, Chicago suburbs.

The Pantana Family, a mixed gospel quartet (Phil and Joy, his brother John, and his wife, Linda), made recordings, and sang on the Old Time Gospel Hour TV Program with Dr. Jerry Falwell, Sr., telecast from

Thomas Road Baptist Church in Lynchburg, VA, where 'Big Jerry' was the pastor.

Phil has four sons and eight grandchildren. They all live in Lynchburg, VA.

CPSIA information can be obtained
at www.ICGtesting.com
Printed in the USA
LVHW051058070322
712798LV00007B/322